Olabode Ogunlana

Olabode Ogunlana, B.A.(Hons), M.A., M.B.A. is a Chartered Insurance Practitioner. He was the first Nigerian Managing Director of the National Insurance Corporation of Nigeria. Since his retirement from active insurance work the author has devoted much time to the study of Yoruba Culture and Language.

GW00671813

THE QUEST FOR
THE RARE LEAF
AND OTHER YORUBA TALES

Books of Africa

Publisher: Books of Africa Ltd

16 Overhill Road

East Dulwich

London SE22 0PH

United Kingdom

Website: www.booksofafrica.com

Email: admin@booksofafrica.com

      sales@booksofafrica.com

Copyright © Olabode Ogunlana 2013

ISBN 978-0-9926863-2-1

A CIP catalogue record for this book is available from the British Library.

Printed in India by Imprint Digital Ltd.

Books of Africa

DEDICATION

This book is dedicated to His Royal Majesty Oba Okunade Sijuwade, Olubuse II, The Ooni of Ife, the spiritual head of the Yoruba people.

And also to my late paternal grandparents, Ogunlana Eleku and Molaye, his wife who introduced me to the lore and culture of oral storytelling.

THE QUEST FOR THE RARE LEAF
AND OTHER YORUBA TALES

OLABODE OGUNLANA

CONTENTS

PREFACE

Yoruba, one of the major languages of West Africa, with approximately fifty million speakers, has down the ages been primarily an oral language: it only effectively came into a written form from the mid-nineteenth century, initially through the work of missionaries.

The author's father, a former school teacher, though not explicitly an anti-colonialist, brought his children up to value the indigenous culture, its language and its oral storytelling traditions, at a time when the culture was marginalised and undervalued. In his childhood, in the 1930s and 1940s, the author experienced at first hand, what in orality studies would be called the interface between primary oral culture and narrative, as understood within the western tradition.

There is a rich tradition of storytelling within Yoruba culture, with stories passed down through the generations but never written down, which is still underexplored by modern scholars. This book sets out to present a particular sub-group of these: oral stories which have some kind of historical basis, handed down in the Ogere-Remo area (now in Ogun State) in the Remo dialect of Yoruba.

As originally told, within the primary oral culture, such stories assumed that those listening would know the culture and traditions within which they originally arose and were passed on. A non-Yoruba reader cannot have that knowledge, but within the fast-evolving cultural and linguistic situation in south-western Nigeria today many Yoruba people, especially young people, are also experiencing that culture far less intimately or are simply losing touch with it altogether. In this context, to set down these stories in print for the first time becomes an act of "translation" not simply from the Ogere-Remo oral dialect into written English, but from the original cultural context of the story into a form that can make sense to a wider audience.

This work studies the problematic of this. It also examines in detail the author's own experience of the orality-literature interface in the context of the way in which Yoruba culture was undervalued in the colonial period and the subsequent rise of Yoruba studies. His research brings forward four Yoruba oral stories into a written form for the first time. The original stories had no titles, but here they are called "The Quest for the Rare Leaf". "The Legend of the Queen's Basket", "The Legend of Orunmila" and "The Ebiripo Episode." The context and background of each of these stories has been thoroughly researched prior to their transformation into modern literary form.

At the heart of the work is the author's desire that the Yoruba oral tradition of storytelling should be reappraised and preserved before it suffers any more erosion. The work provides glimpses into a rich oral storytelling tradition and will hopefully provoke others to work in this important area.

Some of the more modern stories featured in the second part of this book are not merely to amuse; more importantly they are intended to remind us of the high ideals of our forebears and to encourage us to transmit them to those who follow us. The last two stories are not at all traditional but are included to show the changes, sometimes imperceptible, in our beliefs and attitudes since our contact with the outside world.

Olabode Ogunlana

THE QUEST FOR THE RARE LEAF

Introduction

I vividly remember the return of cousin Sode who
had been away in Burma serving in the West African
Frontier Force. The school had just closed for the
day. As we were coming out of the main gate leading into
Broad Street some soldiers came marching along, towards
the Racecourse. They were led by the military band. As
the soldiers marched past the High School I saw him. At
first I thought I was dreaming ... but it was cousin Sode
all right. When I shouted his name he turned his face to
the right to see who was calling. He could not wave to me
but his face lightened and I knew he had seen me. Most
of us ran after the marching soldiers. At the Racecourse
the Governor-General inspected the returning troops.
When the parade was dismissed I rushed up to Sode.
At first he lifted me up, then he put me down and we
hugged each other. We then moved towards the army
lorries parked near the cricket ground. After collecting
his kit we walked all the way home, traversing half of
Broad Street, from the General Hospital near the Colonial
Church down to the Supreme Court Buildings on Tinubu

Square, where we turned off into Alli Street. We took the short-cut through Edwin Lane behind the C.M.S. Church which led us into Isaleagbede Street, then into Aroloya Street and finally into Ojo-Giwa Street.

Great excitement greeted our entry into the compound. Nobody knew that the soldiers were to arrive that day, and there was a great hum of surprise. Family and neighbours all wanted to shake hands and talk with cousin Sode. Being the very first person to see him and to escort him home gave me a sense of pride. I took his kit into his room. I replaced my Win-the-War hat with his army felt hat which nearly covered my entire face. My Win-the-War hat was cheap and made of raffia palm; it had replaced the boater hat which could no longer be imported because of the war. With so many handshakes I feared that Sode's right arm might be wrenched from his shoulder. Everyone wanted to hear about his experiences in Burma. He recounted how they were taken by boat from Ehingbeti Wharf on the Marina to Freetown in Sierra Leone, where all the soldiers from the British West African colonies had converged. They then travelled in a large troopship to Burma. With the three stripes on his arms, we watched him with pride as he told his story. Somehow all kinds of food, palm-wine and soft drinks appeared. An impromptu party started which went on far into the night. Poor cousin Sode was barraged with questions which went on until we all eventually went to bed in the early hours of the next morning. Fortunately it was a Saturday, and we did not need to wake up early. Cousin Sode decided that he would stay on in Lagos for some days to collect his discharge papers and pay-packet as well as to make some purchases before leaving for Ogere to see his family. Among other things, he bought an HMV gramophone and a Raleigh bicycle with speed gears, which at the time was a sign of opulence.

I was unable to have cousin Sode to myself until Sunday evening. I then requested him to remind me of Grandpa's story about Malomo the herbalist. As he seemed not to remember it, I had to prompt him. Even then he thought the story was about Bere and the bondsman. His recollection seemed hazy, like mine. So he suggested that we should ask my father who must have heard the story several times. When we both approached my father he promised to oblige us on the following day as it was already late. He also added that it was a long story.

The following day I reminded Dad, who was commonly known as Eseso, about his promise. He said that the story did not originate from Eleku, his late father. Grandpa had heard the story from Nodu Amoye, his own father. His father's full name was Gusennodu but as was customary in Remo it had been shortened. Dad said that, according to Nodu, the events which gave rise to the story took place some ten years before Eko – as Lagos was then called - was ceded to Queen Victoria. He then told us his version of Eleku's story.

From time to time, in those far off days, traders, both women and men, from all over Remo, made the hazardous journey to Lagos to sell *gari*, palm-oil, yams, *afon*, *esuru*, rice and other farm products and to bring back with them cloth, rare trinkets, mirrors, coral beads and such like things. The men would buy farm tools and building materials – corrugated iron sheets, for example – intending to sell them, although in fact only a few could afford them as most houses at that time were thatched. They trekked several days on foot along tortuous narrow footpaths amidst forests and jungles, going via Sagamu and Odogiyan, all the way to Ebute Ikorodu where they joined the *oko-aje*, locally made wooden boats steered by poles, which conveyed them to Lagos. They used to land at Ebute Eiyekole until later when the boats started to moor at Ebute-Ero which was very near the residence of the *Eleko*, the paramount chief of Lagos. At that time Ogere traders were referred to as 'the *Oluwo* Gbuyi's people'. Why will become clear as this story unfolds, said Dad with a smile.

Long before the arrival of the *Gesi* – as the British colonialists were called – the Yoruba had lived in towns. Each town, large or small, had a government of its own. While the *Oba* or king was the ruler, each town in Remo was run by the *Igbimo Ilu* or town council.[1] Now, while the *Oba* as king was the nominal head, the *Igbimo Ilu* governed, both at the legislative and executive levels. The *Oluwo* was head of the *Igbimo*, while the other chiefs – the *Olisa, Asipa, Apena, Likotun,* and *Balogun* as well as others – were its members. The *Igbimo Ilu* had overall authority over all spheres of life within the town including the markets as well as the supervising body, the *pampa*, of which the powerful *Iyaloja* was a member. The occupation of the Ogere people was mainly farming. Among other

---

[1] Before this, the governance of a town was in the hands of the Osugbo which took over from the Agalamasa. Both of these latter bodies were considered by the people led by the Oloritun, the head of a quarter, as being partisan in their dealings; some even regarded them as secret cults.

things, they grew a lot of rice, *esuru*, a type of yam and *afon*, the African breadfruit.

After a little pause Dad said, "Let us now begin the story of The Quest for the Rare Leaf."

* * *

The *Oluwo* of Ogere, Gbuyi, and his deputy, the *Asipa*, had been good friends from childhood. The *Asipa* belonged to the male section of the age-group of which the Oluwo's first wife was leader of the female section. This provided another bond between the two friends. In their desire to strengthen further the bond between them, as well as the bond between their two families, the *Oluwo* and the *Asipa* had agreed that Omoyeni, the *Oluwo*'s first daughter, would in due course marry Yera, the *Asipa*'s first son.

The wealthy and influential *Oluwo* was highly respected not only in Ogere but in all Remo and even as far as Lagos where he had lived with his late father. The Oluwo had four wives of whom Malomo was the first and most senior. Her eldest daughter, Omoyeni, was the one promised as the future bride to Yera, the *Asipa*'s son.

Malomo was a herbalist. She grew herbs as well as other trees with medicinal contents from which she prepared remedies for the cure of ailments and also condiments for cooking. Omoyeni helped her in the business and she had learnt how to grow and use the herbs, particularly for mothers during pregnancy and for the care of mother and child after the delivery. The *Oluwo* had introduced Malomo to contacts in Lagos who bought most her products; thus she had become wealthy in her own right. Gbolaga, called Gbola, an *Iwofa* (bondsman[2]), had been passed to Malomo by the *Oluwo* to assist her with all the hard work requiring male strength. Alimi Alarobo, an intermediary in the trading business, supplier of the best quality woven and dyed cloth *(aso-oke)* to the important personalities in Remo and district, had, from their first meeting in Lagos, become a good friend of the *Oluwo* who was also an important client of Alimi. To expand his business, Alimi had borrowed some money from the *Oluwo*. As was the custom in those days, he had sent his first son to the *Oluwo* to serve him as *Iwofa* for ten years in lieu of repayment of capital and interest. Gbola, who was then 12-years-old, was very handsome, well-built and light in complexion. He was gentle, softly

[2] Tied worker who can only be released by paying back a "bond"

spoken and hard working. Gbola was two years older than Omoyeni. Both of them grew up together like brother and sister under Malomo's care. As constant companions, it was natural enough that they should grow fond of each other.

One morning the *Oluwo* and the *Asipa* set out at dawn to inspect the repairs to a damaged bridge *(afara)* across the Ejigu river. They went by the Oko Ugbodo footpath, narrow, craggy, and twisted with its many bends. To the right were many cocoa trees, and to the left were kola-nut trees. The farms on both sides of the footpath were interspersed with *aiba* leaves, vegetable gardens and various kinds of fruit trees especially pawpaws. The morning was misty. All was silent and quiet. As they walked along, the *Oluwo* broke the silence, by relating the strange dream he had had during the night.

"In my dream Omoyeni, my daughter, was by the stream which ran by Malomo's farm, washing some herbs in a basket. Coming towards her was a frail looking horse with a nondescript rider on it. The horse was trotting slowly and silently, but just before it reached Omoyeni the horse, now a noble looking animal, gathered speed and the rider on top of it

assumed a very different look. He had turned into a tall and handsome man! In the twinkling of an eye the man bent down, swept up Omoyeni onto the charger, and galloped away at a very fast pace. As the horse flew past me I was surprised to observe that rather than being frightened Omoyeni looked elated. She was smiling as she waved to me as if saying goodbye. I woke up bewildered, wondering what this dream meant."

"It's a strange dream", remarked Asipa. "You should consult Adifase."

"I shall certainly do so after the meeting today."

The footpath being narrow and not wanting to

step on any of the newly made heaps for planting yams, the two men proceeded one behind the other, the *Oluwo* leading the way. As they approached their destination they started to hear voices, those of members of Taiye's age-group, conversing among themselves. It was the *Egbe*'s turn to undertake the repairs to the dislodged bridge and also to maintain the footpath and clear the undergrowth from along the approach pathway leading to the bridge. The swollen river had caused a lot of damage. As the two chiefs came close, the young men at work prostrated themselves and gave the usual greetings.

"Where is your *Jagun* (leader)?" asked the *Oluwo*.

"He is on the other side testing the strength and efficacy of the lashings and straps", answered one of them.

"Which age-group is responsible for the stretch between the bridge and Akamiko?" enquired the Asipa. "That's Oye's age-group, but they are not due to start work until after the next market day."

The two elders expressed appreciation for the work being done as well as for its quality as they took their leave.

'Olipakala a gbe wven' ('Our founder will continue to

24

support you'), added the *Oluwo*.

As the two elders left the Oko Ugbodo footpath and headed for the town the *Oluwo* suggested that they should seize the opportunity to call on the age-group at work on the new sanitation enclosure. By now the light which heralded a new dawn was ablaze in all its glory. The risen sun had dispersed the mists and all the dewdrops on the leaves of the cocoa trees in the farmsteads had started to dry up. Egbe Salau, whose turn it was to work on the sanitation ground, was already there. One group was digging the holes for the compost while the other was busy trimming off the twigs and leaves from the felled tree trunks. The usual greetings were exchanged between the elders and the youngsters who made the customary salute and doffed their caps. After a brief inspection they entered the town by Panoda market so they could see the members of the *pampa* who were already at work. The *Iyaloja* was in charge that day. The usual greetings ensued with the men prostrating themselves and the women kneeling to show respect for the chiefs. Soon work resumed. The various food items were inspected for quality. Gari (cassava flour) and palm-oil were tasted and other farm-products examined. After the inspection, the two chiefs separated. Both later came back for the meeting of the council.

When the meeting was over, the *Oluwo* went to see Adifase, the town's leading *babalawo*, its Ifa priest and diviner. As the *Oluwo* knocked at the door he called out, "Adifase, I hope you are in."

"I am home, *Oluwo*. I hope all is well", replied the *babalawo*.

"I am here to ensure that all will continue to be well," replied the Oluwo. After the exchange of greetings, both of them repaired to the thatched-roofed hut overlooking the fields.

"What is this urgent matter that has brought the *Oluwo* himself to me? Your coming out here is strange. Usually you send for me."

"On this occasion it has to be so. As the elders say, 'When an adult is seen taking giant strides he is either chasing something or something is chasing him.' Besides, 'It is he who has a thorn in his foot who visits the one with a knife.' Overnight I had a dream which puzzled and frightened me."

"Let's have it! This is why Orunmila (the Yoruba god of divination and wisdom) lives here."

When the *Oluwo* had related his dream Adifase

went into his room to fetch the sack which contained his divining equipment, his *opele*. As the *Oluwo* was sitting on the only *ipeku* (stool) in the room, Adifase spread out a mat to sit on. He removed his cap *(abeti-aja)* before throwing the *opele* on the mat. Then a puzzled expression appeared on his face. He threw the *opele* again and again. When he looked up he asked, "*Oluwo asape*, are you by any chance contemplating doing something contrary to the traditions of this community?"

"No," replied the surprised *Oluwo*.

Once more Adifase threw the *opele*. He looked up.

"Are you sure? Ifa says that as custodian of our tradition you are trying to bend it to suit yourself! Please explain this."

"Would Ifa be referring to the arrangement between me and the *Asipa*?"

"What is that about? Please explain."

"I hoped that Omoyeni, my *Bere*, would in due course marry Yera, the *Asipa's Dawodu*, to further strengthen the friendship which has existed since our boyhood days."

"Has Yera shown an interest in Omoyeni?"

"Not really. We both just felt that it would be a

good match."

"*Oluwo*, you and *Asipa* need to take great care and tread carefully. Not all things desirable are permissible, otherwise customs, traditions and culture would never have come into existence. Half a word is enough for the wise! Don't overstep the bounds. In the interest of the community let things take their normal course." So cautioned the Ifa priest.

"Thank you very much," answered the *Oluwo*. He was thoughtful as he left Adifase's abode.

* * *

Malomo, the *Oluwo*'s senior wife, had her main farm about three miles from town. It was quite large and extended over many acres. She cultivated all sorts of herbs and trees with medicinal properties for the production of medicines and spices. While Gbola would undertake the heavy duties – digging, planting, cutting, pounding and drying the roots and bark before making them into paste or powder – while Omoyeni would attend to the winnowing, grinding, and sifting. Malomo herself handled the treating, steaming, and mixing, and the general preparations were undertaken at *oko etile* (a farm) behind their compound in town.

There was a good rapport between Omoyeni and Gbola. The two became close and constant companions, so much so that they soon fell in love, what with the *Bere*[3] already behaving like a seductive young girl and the flame of manhood already starting to stir in Gbola's loins. When Malomo became ill, an illness which became protracted, and she was almost crippled with arthritis, she could no longer go to the main farm. Thus it fell on Omoyeni and Gbola to run the business, with overall supervision in Omoyeni's hands. She pointed out to Gbola which root was to be pounded, which was to be shredded, and so on. After the day's hard work Omoyeni, dainty maiden that she was, bathed herself in the stream behind the farm before completing her toilet, which comprised rubbing her skin with *ori* (shea butter), applying ground *osun* (a paste obtained from African rosewood) to the base of her feet, and the *tiroo* (galena, made with lead sulphide to brighten them) between her eyelids. Gbola in the meantime busied himself cleaning and storing the implements and tools, and preparing the bundles and baskets of herbs ready to take home.

On one such occasion Gbola heard Omoyeni yelling

[3] *Bere* is the name given to the eldest daughter in a family

29

for him. She had twisted her ankle while getting out of the stream and was lying on the grassy bank in great pain. Gbola found her there, naked, writhing in agony. He quickly fetched a mat, laid her on it and dried her with one of her wrappers. Covering her with the wrapper he quickly uprooted some giant *gbegi* grass, ground its bulb into paste and mixed this with shea butter. With this mixture he started to rub and massage her ankle as well as her leg. While he did so Omoyeni started to moan, though not entirely in pain. In fact it was less agony and more passion: her desirable thin lips were quivering. Slowly, the moaning turned to gasping. Then she started to whisper, "It's so soothing, don't stop, please continue. It's so soothing and pleasing; please move upwards, yes, up my leg, up and up." And she started to coo like a dove.

It was a very cool harmattan evening. Omoyeni whispered, 'I am cold. Please carry me into the hut, I need some warmth.' As Gbola gently lifted her, and nestled her in his arms and against his chest, Omoyeni clung tightly onto Gbola's neck. The position being so comfortable and cosy, Omoyeni implored Gbola to leave her there awhile. Contented, Omoyeni continued to moan; then her body started to pulsate slowly. As Gbola bent down to lower her onto the mat, Omoyeni's hold on his neck became tighter. The pulsation became more pronounced and her face had a sweet broadened smile. Her lips parted and her whispers became inaudible. In that moment she became bewitching and everything became blurred. The embers of affection that had smouldered for so long were ignited in a flash. The flame sparked. The accident then turned into an incident: Omoyeni the maiden was transformed into a woman. From that day onwards Omoyeni started to glow and to purr, especially whenever the two were alone. For his part Gbola doted on her even more, anticipating her every wish.

* * *

Six weeks later Omoyeni discovered she was pregnant. In trepidation she told Malomo about the accident and the incident on the farm. While showing her dismay, her mother was in fact inwardly pleased, for she did not approve of the proposed union between the pretty, dainty Omoyeni and Yera, the crude and lazy bore. Besides, she was fond of Gbola. At the same time she was apprehensive of the scandal that would ensue, especially in such a small community. How would she and Omoyeni live it down? The shame would kill them both. Then another thought surged to the front of her mind. How would her husband, the *Oluwo*, react, with his strict adherence to traditional customs and values?

Almost certainly, the heavens would fall! However, Malomo was consoled by the fact by insisting on the union of Yera and Omoyeni he had not followed tradition and many had started to whisper. 'Maybe it is all for the good,' she thought quietly. And suddenly she became silent, lost in deep thought, while Omoyeni looked on anxiously. Then she smiled and said to her daughter, "For the time being keep quiet. I know what to do. Off with you. I will see you later. In the meantime, you and Gbola must behave normally and go about your work as usual. Until I sort this out, both of you should spend more time on the farm."

Then, still deep in thought, Malomo started her plan. She said to herself, 'Asipa, my age-mate, is *Oluwo*'s best friend as well as his confidant. He is the key to the solution. He will assist me. I shall lure him with something delectable. But first I must fire Yera's longing for the best prize. I shall do more.

Yera must be stampeded into immediate marriage with Omoyeni. As a bait I shall dangle before Yera the prospect of marriage with Oburo. That will take place soon after the first one with Omoyeni. With that, Yera will understand and will not even want to consummate his first marriage – if it can be called that – and Omoyeni will be left unmolested to continue in the herb garden. There is nothing new in having two wives at the same time. With help from me, he will have the means he needs for that.'

Accordingly, she sent for Yera at a time when Omoyeni was away at the farm. Before then she had requested her niece, Oburo Orokelewa (the fair beauty), to come and cook the lunch for her visitor. She had also primed this pretty girl to take exceptional care with her toilet and put on an elegant head-tie. She confided in her niece that the intention was to turn Yera's head. The innocent and unsuspecting girl opened her eyes wide in amazement.

"Auntie, that is the young groom intended for Omoyeni."

"Shut up and do as you're told. Don't you want an ideal groom like him - and he's the son of the *Asipa*?"

At first Oburo smiled coyly but then she reacted: "'I

don't want to pinch Omoyeni's man! I love my cousin."

Malomo replied sharply, "Are you deaf, do as you're told." Then, with her mesmerising smile: "You will never regret it. Omoyeni and I will always be grateful to you. We shall contribute generously to your trousseau. You will be the envy of all the other girls."

And so Yera came to lunch. He greatly enjoyed the meal with Malomo and Oburo; perhaps even more, he enjoyed the company, the smiles and the attention of Malomo's niece. After the meal when Oburo had retired to the backyard to wash the dishes Yera asked shyly who the sweet young maiden was.

"Do you like her? Isn't she prettier and more pleasant than haughty Omoyeni?"

"She is indeed lovely. No one could see her and not desire her." Yera's eyes were glowing.

"She is my niece and the Apena's daughter. If you really prefer her I can persuade her to consider your suit. More than that, I can persuade Omoyeni to give you up for her," she said with her sweet, crafty smile.

"Please do so. For this elegant prize I shall do whatever you and Omoyeni want. The only difficulty I see is my father. He has set his mind on my union with Omoyeni. Can you handle that as well?"

Malomo whispered silently to herself, '*Awodi to nre Ibara, efufu ta n'dipe o ni okuku mu ise ya,*' that is to say, 'The tail of the hawk that is bound for Ibara is lifted by the wind; it says "Now to business".' An order to do what we want to do anyway hardly needs encouragement!

With a big smile Malomo said, "Just leave it all to me. I know your taste. You know how close your late mother was to me. Let's just say I am representing her. I shall talk to the *Asipa*, but a little cunning will be required. To compensate Omoyeni you will agree that the marriage with her will take place very soon. Of course you realise that there will be no consummation. You will be keeping her safe from scandal and for Gbola, so to say," she added with a wink. "Soon after that your true wedding with the one you love will take place. Oh, what a joy that will be! It is not new in our society to take two wives almost at the same time. The generous gifts of money from Omoyeni and me will enable you to bear the expense of keeping them both. You will be the envy of your age-mates who have been sneering at you."

Yera left in a happy daze and with great anticipation!

* * *

The next victim of Malomo's guile was Apena, Oburo's father. Malomo had no difficulty with him, because of his ambitions for himself and his pretty daughter. Anyway he thought that becoming an in-law to the highly favoured *Asipa*, next in command to *Oluwo* himself was worth any sacrifice. To further soften Apena's mind and make him more pliable, Malomo said with a very crafty smile, "Apena, let us be honest with ourselves. The procedure by which matches are now arranged for young couples without regard to their feelings, and without consultation with them, is foreign to our custom. How compatible is it with the tradition of our ancestors? How fair is it to the young ones? After all, the youngsters will spend all their lives together. Shouldn't they have a say in the matter? You know the old custom. After a young man has fallen for someone, he will request his parents to ask an *alarena* (marriage intermediary) to undertake the necessary enquiries as to the suitability of the girl for marriage. How wise our forefathers were! At no time did Yera tell the *Asipa* that he was interested in

Omoyeni, whereas he had been singing the praises of Oburo and hankering after her. You have confirmed that he has opened his heart to you about this. Please give Oburo your support; the two are in love. What can be better than such a match? Arrange for your *alarena* to get on with her duties."

The approach to *Asipa* was subtle. Prompted by Malomo, Yera requested his father to ask *Oluwo* for an early marriage between him and Omoyeni. When approached in this way the unsuspecting *Asipa* was overjoyed. He readily agreed, as his dream, in spite of the murmurs of the detractors, was about to come true. Even when he became aware of his son's interest in Oburo, he brushed it aside. He thought to himself, 'One cannot account for the whims of this new generation!' Suddenly his son, who had never shown much interest in anything, now wanted for himself two of the most attractive young women in the community! He concluded that as long as his wishes and those of his best friend were met, it did not matter if Yera took a second wife. Omoyeni, *Oluwo*'s *Bere,* would in reality be a mere second. In addition he would have both the *Oluwo* and Apena as in-laws! What could be better?

As for the *Oluwo,* there was no impediment since

he had set his mind on the union. As a result he readily agreed. Thus the marriage between Yera and Omoyeni took place.

The storm broke when Omoyeni's son was born early. Such a premature birth, by almost two months, seemed very strange to the community. The *Oluwo* became suspicious. He asked questions and made enquiries. Although he is regarded as the custodian of the community's tradition he could not afford to examine this matter closely since he had compromised himself by not honouring tradition over Yera's union with Omoyeni. So he gave in easily in order to avoid a scandal. However, all too soon he learnt that Gbola was the father of Omoyeni's son! He became furious.

'Here is a more serious scandal,' thought the *Oluwo*. 'How can a mere *Iwofa*, a bondsman, become father of my grandson? Such a catastrophe must be prevented at all cost.' He then took a very rash decision. He asked Gbola to leave the town immediately to go and procure for him *ewe mi riyiri*, the rare leaf. The elders knew that in reality Gbola was being sent into exile, never to return. He had been sent on a quest that was bound to fail, for no such leaf in fact existed. ....Very few people knew the background story.

Oburo's marriage to Yera had been celebrated after his first wedding with Omoyeni. Yera and Oburo were greatly in love and, because they knew the true state of affairs between Yera and Omoyeni, , they went off to live happily forgetting all about Omoyemi whom most people believed was Yera's senior wife. 'Let her busy herself with her herbs while leaving us to enjoy our match,' seemed to sum up their attitude. As for poor Gbola, he started to wander from village to village and from town to town, on the fruitless quest for the 'rare leaf'.

* * *

For seven long months Gbola travelled on many dusty, rugged and twisting footpaths. He had seen more villages, hamlets and towns than he had ever thought to see in his life. He started to get weary and frustrated. Omoyeni and their little son were always in his thoughts. Towards evening one day as he was ascending a hill he decided to rest. He came to a big *araba*, a white silk cotton tree as the sun was setting. The many colours of the setting sun – golden yellow tinged with orange, light grey, and crimson –

gladdened his heart and put new life and hope into him. He remembered what they said the Ifa oracle had predicted about his life. Would it ever come to pass? he wondered. He was musing about this when he thought he heard someone sighing - or perhaps it was just his imagination. Then he heard the sound again. It was followed clearly by a voice.

"Who is there? What are you doing in this lonely spot so late in the evening?"

Gbola tip-toed silently to see who it was. Reclining against the tree was a cheerful looking man, smiling to himself.

Gbola addressed him: "Who are you too? And if you don't mind me asking, what are you doing in this lonely place?"

The merry faced man, still smiling, answered calmly, "I am *Eniko o mo,* messenger of the *Irunmales* (Yoruba gods), and it is my business to move around the country. You look so weary. Fortunately you are near a haven of rest, but you won't find the way unless I point you in the right direction." With a twinkle in his eye he continued, "When you get to the top of the hill you will see a clump of thick *koko* leaves, green, large and lush, on your left. Push them aside. You will come into an open space. Follow the narrow footpath. It will lead you to the home of an old wise man. There you will find shelter for the night and much more."

Before Gbola could thank him the stranger jumped up, whistling a funny tune and disappeared into the approaching night.

Although Gbola was doubtful about the man's sanity, he decided to put his suggestion to the test. Sure enough he found the cottage. He was very tired and footsore. He was about to collapse when he saw an old man dressed all in white, with hair and a beard both also completely white. He was reclining on a *taraga (a* couch made with cane). On seeing Gbola's condition the old man quickly called for someone from within to come out and assist the staggering stranger. There was a prompt response. When the stranger had been seated the old man requested some cold water to be brought for him. Though Gbola wanted to speak, the old man signalled that he should hold his peace.

"You must be really exhausted. Please rest and get back your breath before speaking. You must be famished too."

He then called for food enough for two. Again Gbola indicated his wish to speak. "Not yet. You can speak after the meal, not before," said the aged man.

Before long two women appeared carrying earthenware bowls and platters. They were placed on an *ipeku* (stool) in front of the old man. A big earthenware bowl of water was brought to enable the two to wash their hands. The old man asked Gbola to proceed, but he invited the old man to do so first. The old man smiled and washed his hands. Then Gbola did the same. When the remnants of the meal had been cleared away the old man asked for a gourd of palm-wine to be brought. A young man came in with a gourd and two drinking calabashes. First he prostrated himself before the old man, then he squatted and poured the two calabashes full with white froth, before handing them over with a bow, first to the old man and then to Gbola. They were then left alone.

For the first time Gbola observed his surroundings. The moon was already high in the sky; the stars were twinkling; the breeze was cool and fresh. The serenity here was astounding: there were palm trees, sugar-cane stems, bananas, plantains and other forms of vegetation. There were very tall, ancient-looking trees, the tallest being a white silk cotton tree with immense girth and leafy, majestic branches. The old man then motioned to

Gbola that he should now speak. So Gbola told his story, starting from the very beginning. After hearing him out the old man sighed deeply and shook his head.

Pointing to his head the old man asked, "What do you see here?"

"Hair, white like cotton," replied Gbola.

Again the old man pointed to his chin and asked "And this?"

"A white beard, full and long."

"You are right, my son. But what do they stand for?"

"It is obvious, revered father, that you are very old. Your face has the stamp of age and wisdom."

The old man nodded. *"Beni, Ewu logbo, irugbon lagba* (Yes, wisdom comes with age). Indeed, as one goes along the journey of life one picks up events and experiences which later become stories to be told when one gets old – making history, one might say. If I tell you what I have been through before attaining this ripe age and acquiring this white hair, you might pray to die young! So I won't." He was still smiling. "A man must learn to bear the burden of life with courage. Intuition tells me that you have before you a glorious life and future. The *Oluwo* must have felt deeply offended to send you on this fruitless quest." And now he chuckled. "Whenever an elder requests someone to go in search of the 'rare leaf' it means 'get lost in exile and never come back.'" Then he added, "*ogbon ki i tan l'aiye k'awa lo s'orun* (the world cannot become bereft of wisdom to entail a journey to heaven). For now, go in and have a good night's rest. We shall discuss things further in the morning."

The sage was already reclining on his *taraga*, a cane couch, when Gbola made his appearance next morning. It was a beautiful day. The sun was just rising. It was cool and calm. The birds had started chirping. There was peace and quiet, which reminded Gbola of the haven to which Eniko o mo made reference. He was marvelling at the world around him when he remembered where he was, prostrated himself before the old man and in response to his greetings and enquiries as to whether he had slept well and had breakfast he answered in the affirmative.

"My son, go to the *Iroko* tree in front of you. Underneath it is what looks like a thick shrub. Bring me one of its twigs with as many leaves as possible. Tomorrow, dry the leaves in the sun. Do so every day until they become very dry. Then take the dried leaves to the *Oluwo* and tell him, "I cannot find the 'rare leaf', but in its place, here is a leaf equally valuable. It is called *Ewe kagba gba a, kowo, koye. Gbigba lagba ngha a,* meaning an elder overlooks a troubling and baffling episode. That, my son, will be the end of the matter."

Then the old man asked Gbola to kneel in front of him. Placing his two hands on Gbola's head, he blessed him. "You are a very fortunate young man, Omoluwabi[4]. Go in peace. Wealth, honour and peace will be your lot. The Almighty Father will be your support and defence all the days of your life. Amen."

He then took an *ado,* a miniature gourd containing a potion, from underneath his seat.

"Take this valuable medication. You will need it soon. Whenever you are told that a person is suffering from a disease without cure then give it to that person. Put sixteen drops of it into *eko* (steamed maize flour) and mix it with water for the person to drink. The person who drinks this will not only become well but will become new again. Guard it. It is precious. Continue on this footpath before you until you get into a glade. From the height you will see a valley. Go there. Good fortune awaits you there." Once again Gbola prostrated himself before the old man and thanked him profusely.

[4] The name means "from the stem of Noah"

Now he walked briskly and confidently along. Very soon he reached the glade mentioned by the old man. The sun was blazing but due to the shade provided by the trees the whole place was cool. The sky was clear and blue. The local birds, *elulu*, *orofo*, *adaba*, and *atiala-atioro*[5] were flitting from tree to tree. The setting was so serene and inviting. This would have been a good place to rest, thought Gbola, but his mission gave no room for rest. As the old man had said, the plateau overlooked a very beautiful vista. Right before him was a farm in a valley. He could see a number of people in it; from where he stood they looked so small. Beyond the farm some thatch-roofed huts dotted the area. Eager to reach the farm to test the truth of the old man's words, he quickened his pace as he descended. Soon after, he reached the entrance to the farm. A man standing there seemed to be expecting someone. Before Gbola could speak the man asked if he was the man sent from the vegetable farm. Gbola answered in the negative. "Then you must be one of those men seeking work here." Gbola replied that he was new in the village, adding that he could do with a job. The man informed him that the place was a special farm devoted to growing herbs, medicinal trees and plants.

[5] The Senegal Coucal, Sierra Leone Green Fruit Pigeon, West African Red-eyed Turtle Dove and the Allied Hornbill

46

Gbola smiled saying that this had been his occupation for the last ten years. He was invited in to meet the owner of the farm. First the man went into a room and Gbola could hear him talking with two people, a man and a woman. He was then invited in. A young lady, with a puzzled look, was sitting in front of a long trestle on which there were many plants and herbs.

"We are told you know about herbs," said the lady.

"Yes," replied Gbola.

He was then invited to move nearer and help identify the plants on the trestle. Gbola moved closer, wondering what was afoot. Seeing the look on Gbola's face the lady went on to explain that the man in charge of the farm had suddenly fallen ill and although they were the owners of the farm they did not know much about herbs. Gbola then sorted out the herbs. He asked for water to sprinkle on some of them. "The others would need to be soaked," he added. After some discussion on the growing of herbs and their treatment Gbola was conducted round the large farm which appeared to be flourishing. He was persuaded to stay the night with the couple so that they could resume their talk the next day. On the following day Gbola agreed to stay only for a month or two. All too

soon he had forgotten the old man's prediction.

The elderly man was in fact merely visiting the farm to assist his niece to get settled and take charge. Now that an expert had been found he planned to leave soon, which he did. As agreed, Gbola began work at the farm the next day. Watching how Gbola set to work and how he got on with the workforce, the woman was highly impressed. Later that evening the lady made an attractive offer, asking Gbola to stay indefinitely to help organise the farm and make it more profitable. She offered Gbola half of the resulting profit. She went on to explain that after the death of the farmer the family had wanted to sell the farm, but now she had found an expert she would stay on, learn on the job and become an expert herself, so that she could then run the farm when Gbola eventually left. Gbola agreed to stay for a while. He taught the workers all about herbs: when, how, and where to grow all the species; how to harvest them, and the various processes; the treatments required; storage and everything else that needed to be done. Above all, Gbola promised to introduce them to buyers who knew the value of good herbs.

Gbola had been given a hut to live in. After a year he felt that he had saved enough to repay what his father owed to the *Oluwo* should this be necessary, as well as to pay for the dowry and other expenses of the marriage with Omoyeni. When he mentioned his plan to leave, the lady looked sad. She requested Gbola to stay on as she would be unable to run the farm without him. Later that evening she came to Gbola's hut to discuss 'a very important issue', as she put it. She came straight to the point: "Gbola, you have great expertise with herbs and your skill with people is excellent. Under you the farm has taken a turn for the better. All the employees are happy working under you. You have shown me the value of what we have in this farm and that we are on to something important here. I am being candid, *tomo eni ba da a ka so* (do not hesitate to praise a good person). We are both single and, although it is unheard of for a woman to propose to a man, my desire is that we get married. Then you will never have to leave *Ido Oyin*, this farm and me."

Gbola was taken aback. He explained that the reason he wished to leave was to return to his beloved fiancée and their child from whom he had been separated for almost two years. The lady seemed stunned. "All the workers say you are unmarried. Are you saying all this to put me off? Am I not beautiful enough? I have no ties whatsoever with anyone in the world. I know my proposal is odd and sudden. Please think about it overnight," she pleaded. Gbola replied gently: "There is nothing to think over. I have told the truth." To Gbola's embarrassment the lady broke down and started to sob. After calming down she appeared to have dropped asleep. Gbola had to tap her on the shoulder. "Let me walk you to your hut. We shall talk some more tomorrow." All she could do was nod. She walked as if she was half asleep while Gbola supported her.

The next day, first thing in the morning, Gbola

called on her. He asked her not to be despondent. He offered to go to his home and talk to his fiancée to try to convince her so his family could come and settle at Ido Oyin provided they could jointly own the farm on an equal basis. Morin, for that was the name of the lady, beamed with a smile. She said, "You mean that, honestly? You are not running away." "No, I assure you," was Gbola's reply.

* * *

To the consternation of Malomo, and others within the household, late one evening the *Oluwo* suddenly felt very ill. Malomo thought that he was suffering from *lofutu*, arthritis, and treated him accordingly. They all went to bed in great anxiety. First thing next morning Malomo went into his room to enquire about his illness. *Oluwo*'s said he felt much the same as the previous evening, only now he could not lift his right arm, which felt wholly lifeless. Malomo made the observation that it was obviously not *lofutu*, as the balm comprising of ground *gbegi* bulb and *ori* would have made him better. She added that she had requested Omoyeni, who was now as knowledgeable as herself, to come and examine the *Oluwo*. As they were talking Omoyeni entered. After a brief examination she confirmed that it was not *lofutu*. She suggested that Tunda, the traditional doctor, be invited to see her father. He agreed and asked that Malomo should also send for Adifase, the Ifa priest. As father and daughter sat silently the *Oluwo* said this: "Omoyeni, you still wear this grief on your face even after almost two years. Something tells me that all will be well. Cheer up."

They agreed that the Oluwo's ailment was not *lofutu*. "What it is, I do not know. Let's wait and hear what Adifase has to say." Not long afterwards Adifase arrived. After his normal greeting he added, "The *Irunmales* will support us. Lipakala will uphold us." He spread out his mat and produced from his pouch the *opele*. He whispered into it before the first throw; then he made a second and a third throw.

Looking up he blurted out, "'Ha! Ha! I said so! May the *Irunmales* forgive you, *Oluwo*! But for Malomo your suffering could have been worse. What you called her guile was what reduced your pain. Ifa says you will get well. Malomo, our good mother, I and Orunmila thank you."

He continued, "The *orisas* and *Irunmales*, guardian spirits of this town and the entire community, have levelled three charges against you. Firstly, your treatment of Omoyeni and Gbola was uncalled for. Gbola was no ordinary bondsman. You assured his father, Alimi, your friend, that Gbola would be treated as your own child. You gave him your word. Yes, a worthless *Iwofa* may be sent into an exile of no return, but no sane person would throw out a ward. Secondly, you forced Omoyeni and Yera into a union distasteful to them both which was not in accordance with our custom and tradition – you, the *Oluwo Asape*, custodian of Ogere culture! Thirdly, you acted contrary to what fate had decreed for Yera and Gbola. Everyone, including the *Asipa*, Yera's father, knew the type of person he was. He was lazy and cowardly, so much so that he refused to train or serve as a warrior. He had been so petted and cuddled he behaved like a spoilt child! Our elders said *Ile ni iku wa l'eran Ajayi; Ayanmo-ipin eran Olugbode*: 'The-home-is-where-death-lurks, the name of Ajayi's goat; One's-fate-is-set-at-one's-creation, the name of Olugbode's goat.' No one was surprised when he died suddenly in his own home under the *afon* tree. Who are you to alter his fate? As for Gbola, Ifa says that at his birth it was shown that he was a great star who would rise high in the firmament, add lustre to his family heritage, and become a useful citizen of the world. To save your own face you sacrificed him and sent him into exile! This is what you must now do.....

"Send your messengers out to find Gbola and bring him home. After all the necessary preliminaries, hand over Omoyeni to Alimi, to be passed on to Gbola as his wife. To propitiate the *Irunmales* and the Ogere community you will at your own expense procure two hornless cattle which from today will roam around this town as was instructed by Lipakala himself when he founded this city of sixteen rivers and sixteen hills. It is not for nothing that the figure sixteen tallies with Orunmila's sixteen *odus*. *Be e ni; erendogun Ifa ni i fo ire,* meaning only sixteen *odus* can bring good things. This action will promote trade and commerce in this land as well as bringing lasting peace to the community. Orunmila further says that help is at your doorstep and Ifa adds that you will fully recover and give further service to this community. Never again, until you are gathered to the abode of your ancestors, do anything contrary to the traditions of Ogere! *Aki i gbo buruku l'enu abo're. Abo mi re. Lipakala agbeni ma dehin a gbe gbogbo wa. Ase – Amen*: 'He who propitiates the gods never utters evil words. I am done. May Lipakala continue to support and defend us. Amen.' "

At this point Malomo went out to fetch *Oluwo*'s meal. As she got into the yard which separated his quarters and hers, she came face to face with what she thought was an apparition. Her face became drained of blood, and she stared like one seeing a ghost. There was utter silence.

"Elewe omo, it's me, Gbola. I am not a phantom."

Still visibly shaken, Malomo gasped, "Have you found the rare leaf?"

"No, but a sage gave me a substitute which is equally good and perhaps better. Where is the *Oluwo* so I can put it in his hand? Where are Omoyeni and the child?"

"Both are quite well. Come in and see the *Oluwo* who is unwell."

Just then they were interrupted by a wailing noise from under a tree in the compound. Looking in the direction of the noise Gbola saw that it was Oburo. She was sitting on a mat, wailing and weeping and some people were waiting on her. Gbola was informed that Yera had died that morning; a ripe *afon* (African breadfruit) dropped on him and broke his neck. Gbola went over to Oburo, consoled her and handed her over to her age-mates who had come to console her.

At this point there was yet another interruption. Alimi, Gbola's father, entered and asked Malomo what was happening. She told him everything. Just then Omoyeni came out to find out what was delaying her mother. She could not believe her eyes when she saw Gbola! They flew into each other's arms. After calming down they all proceeded into *Oluwo*'s quarters. The once vibrant chief was now laid low with a useless right arm. To their surprise he started to make apologies to both Alimi and Gbola. Adifase, the *babalawo,* then explained what had happened. There and then Gbola asked for cold water and *eko* (steamed ground corn flour wrapped in leaves) to be brought. He prepared a mixture which he passed to the *Oluwo* to drink after his meal. He also made a bowl of it for Malomo. He said this was to be repeated daily, and within three months the *Oluwo* was restored to his former health; Malomo too was healed of her chronic arthritis.

When Gbola, Omoyeni and their son left for Ido

Oyin they were accompanied by Oburo who was now a childless widow. A month earlier Gbola and Omoyeni's marriage had been celebrated. Omorinsola (Morin's name in full) was delighted to welcome Gbola and his family to Ido Oyin. Omorinsola, now Gbola's business partner, later married Gbolawoye, Gbola's younger brother. In this haven of peace Oburo found another husband. The herb business grew enormously, offering employment to many in the village. No one was surprised when Gbola rose to become a chief in Ido Oyin.

Eseso concluded his story with the words *abo mi re*, which means 'Here ends the story.; 'I am done.'

THE LEGEND OF THE QUEEN'S BASKET

When we were children we used to visit the village, often spending the long vacations there during the rainy season. At these times the moon appeared only rarely and when it did we were all so glad. On such nights my grandfather would tell us stories. "I want you to listen to one of them which I found very fascinating," my grandfather said to us on one such night.

My late nephew, Tade, was forever probing and asking about the history of the family. He had a great ally in Iya Alaro (dyer), an old woman who was said to be a distant relation. One time, Tade paid Iya Alaro a visit, a pre-arranged one. He got the usual warm welcome.

"Do you have your writing materials as I directed?" asked the wise old woman. "Yes, revered mother; I have them here," replied the young man. "I also warned my wife that I shall be with you for some time. You may, therefore, proceed. Please take all the time you need."

"Sit down, my son and record the events which took place long before your mother of blessed memory was born. Olabosipo, sometimes called Olabopo (or Labo for short) was the first daughter of Oba Afun. She was generally known and called Bere. In later years she was given the title of custodian of the Queen's Basket. She was a very graceful and beautiful woman. She was as wise as she was fair, and also a dyer of great repute. Legend has it that a goddess taught her. In addition, she excelled in the craft of weaving on the loom the local fabric known as *aso oke*. I was her ward and she taught me the craft of dyeing. That was how I became Iya Alaro. For the sake of completeness I should explain that among the Yoruba all first born females in a family are called Bere while their male counterparts are called Dawodu."

One morning Oba Afun did not emerge as usual from his *akodi* (the inner chamber of the royal apartments). The courtiers and others had been sitting patiently for many hours, some of them since the cock crowed. By then the sun was already overhead, beating mercilessly down on the bald heads of the old, wizened men who formed the majority of the revered assemblage. No man was allowed to wear a cap within the royal precinct. They were at a loss as to what should be done. It is forbidden for anyone to enter the venerated chamber unless sent for. Not even his senior wife, the *Yeye Olori* or indeed his *babalawo* (the king's diviner and priest, also known as *adifa oba*) are allowed to breach the protocol.

In the end it was the *Yeye Olori* who pointed the assemblage in the right direction. "Please send for Bere," she advised, and when she came the situation was explained to her. "As your father's favourite child, we authorise you to enter the chamber to find out what is wrong. We know that it is against tradition, but your father dotes on you. Please save us all from this dreadful suspense. The last time in living memory a similar thing occurred was when the reigning *Afun* joined his ancestors. May the *irunmales* (the Yoruba gods) forbid it on this occasion."

Understandably, it was with great trepidation that Bere entered the royal chamber. The Oba was staring into space. In front of him was an oval shaped raffia basket. The lid was by its side. Bere knelt on her knees with her hands firmly on the ground and her face bent downwards. The Oba appeared to be unaware of the intrusion. The silence was punctuated by ominous sighs and groans issuing forth from *Kabiyesi* (his majesty). After some time had passed, Bere summoned up the courage to whisper, "I hope all is well, *Kabiyesi*? The entire court has been in a state of suspense and fear.

What is the matter? What is the problem? Is wisdom not the daughter of old age? After all, any problem to which you have no solution can only be solved by the *irunmales* (gods) and others in the great beyond."

This appeal evoked a response from *Kabiyesi*. He said: "My daughter, a horrendous thing has happened. All my powers have gone. They have crumbled like dust. Step forward and see for yourself. This kingdom is doomed. My words, hitherto charged with supernatural powers, no longer have force. My *Ase* (potent words) have disappeared. Who has done this? What has caused it? Come forward my daughter and behold with your eyes."

"I dare not," replied Bere. "Who am I to look inside the Queen's basket. Everyone knows its powers. Please, father, do not press me to do this. Just tell me what has happened. Between us and with guidance from the *irunmales* and our ancestors, a satisfactory solution will be found."

"As everyone knows, and as you have testified, this basket is sacred, extremely so," the Oba responded. "It was entrusted to me by my mother, the late Queen. It belonged to her mother before her and her mother before that. It has always been passed down by the reigning

Queen to her successor, from time immemorial."

In reply, Bere observed that if the basket was so ancient and potent why should the contents crumble? Would the physical state of the contents really matter to the extent that it would eradicate or diminish the powers of the contents of the basket?

"I have my doubts, father. What really matters is the strength of your faith, your faith in the powers bequeathed to you by your ancestors."

"You do not understand, my daughter. I derive all my powers from the contents of the basket. Whatever I say when my hands are resting on it will come to pass. If I bless a person the blessing will rest and abide with him or her for all time. Similarly if I curse, the curse will persist. Without the Queen's basket I am nothing. Every morning when I wake, the first thing I do is to touch the basket and pat my bald head with my hands while at the same time blessing myself and asking for the wisdom to undertake all my duties for the day. I have done this for years without ever removing the lid of the basket. Even when I put in new contents the lid will only be half-opened. Because of the weighty issues to be dealt with by the council today I thought I would obtain extra power and discernment by touching the contents. What a costly error," the Oba continued. "I know what the contents are! All I had to do was to lift up the side of the basket and throw in the new package. Instead I touched the contents inside! Let us see now - how many additional packages have I deposited into it during my reign? All told 37 or 38."

"If I may ask, father," said Bere, "how is it that your mother entrusted it to you when the tradition had been that it went down from mother to daughter?"

"I think it was because my mother was greatly fond of me," the Oba replied. "She thought that the powers possessed by the basket would make me a great ruler. Besides, when she was called home to her rest, her Bere, my sister, was away. As you know she got married to the Oba of Ajiran far away in the city beyond the Delta."

"If I may ask, father," his daughter requested, "what do the packets dropped into the basket contain?" *Kabiyesi* then explained: "They are the trophies of the virtue of our womenfolk. Whenever they got married their *ibale* (i.e. *Iba-ni-ile*, the sign of virginity being intact) were sent home as proof of their virtue and the high standard of their upbringing. This was the white cloth stained by blood during consummation of the marriage. I am hoping that after the festival of the new yams when you are married to the tall warrior from the town of sixteen hills and sixteen streams, yours will be added. The *ibale* was regarded as a good omen and it provided a solid foundation for a blissful, fruitful and prosperous marriage. Mothers whose daughters lived up to these high expectations were greatly honoured and applauded. Similarly, such brides were respected by their husbands and by both families. The brides were given valuable presents. Such brides became the envy of all the girls and their parents. How terrible was the ignominy of the bride who proved otherwise! May the *irumales* never inflict such a girl and such ill-luck on our family."

"What preservatives are used to ensure that the cloths remain intact?" asked Bere. "We were told that in ancient times they were soaked in special dyes," the Oba explained, "but over generations the art of making the dyes was lost. The cloths were, therefore, no longer so treated."

"Are you surprised then that they disintegrated? What matters, father, is your faith in the efficacy of the basket and its contents. As I see it, the state of the contents is of no significance. Nevertheless I shall spare no effort in finding the correct dye. As you know I had always assisted grandmother with her herb garden. With a thorough search I shall soon find which roots or leaves or combination of both are used. Now father, replace the lid, put your hands on the basket, pat your head, and bless me. In particular ask the gods to give me the wisdom to detect quickly the right roots and herbs."

Kabiyesi signified his consent with a smile. Then he added that the ancient tradition would be restored there and then. "You, my daughter, as the Bere, will now become the custodian of this powerful and famous basket; but it will be kept in the Senior Wife's quarters. Beres must get married. Then the basket will be inherited by the new Bere. Since it will still remain within the royal compound its power will still be there for me as before. Pick it up my dear child. May the *irunmales* always bless and protect you."

Thereafter the King in all his majesty emerged from his chamber leaning on the arm of his beloved daughter, Bere. The entire court cheered, with all the women kneeling while the men prostrated. The *kakaki* (trumpet) was blaring. This was how Bere became the custodian of the Queen's basket.

———————◆———————

THE QUEST FOR THE RARE LEAF

AND OTHER YORUBA TALES

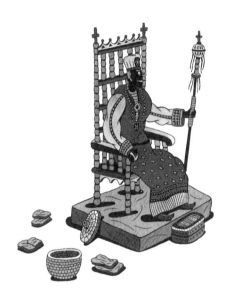

THE LEGEND OF ORUNMILA

Introduction

Rev. Canon John King, chaplain to the Bishop of Lagos, was the director of the Lay Preacher's Course for the 1965-66 session in which I participated. He made it mandatory for every candidate to select and study an aspect of one indigenous religion for the purpose of comparison with Christianity. A brief report of each candidate's findings was to be submitted to him by the end of June 1966; the course ended in September 1966. I decided to study Ifa (the Yoruba god of wisdom and divination), including worship and the act of divination itself. Accordingly, my father arranged for an old friend of his, Pa Fagbemi, an experienced and renowned Ifa priest, to have me as a pupil for six months. Pa Fagbemi was about ten years older than my father, and at that time he had four full-time pupils. I was not part of that group, so he gave me two separate sessions per week, from 3-5pm on Tuesdays and Thursdays. As the men's Bible class in my church was held on Thursdays at 6pm I usually went to the class direct from Pa Fagbemi's residence.

One Thursday I arrived early and spent the waiting period reading my Yoruba Bible. I normally read my Yoruba Bible aloud to myself to ensure that my pronunciation and inflections were correct, as after the course I would be expected to give one sermon every month in Yoruba. It was, therefore, essential that my Yoruba should be perfect, including the usage of appropriate proverbs, adages and sayings. On this occasion I was going through the portion to be studied at the Bible class later that evening, Matthew 6: 25-34. As I reached verse 33, "But seek ye first the kingdom of God, and his righteousness; and all these things shall be added unto you", I heard from Pa's room, his voice being clear and loud, *okare omo; be e gangan lo yo loju opon mi,* meaning "Bless you, my son. That was exactly what was revealed on my divining plate." I smiled and thought to myself, Pa must have misunderstood or misheard what I was reading or he must have been discussing something entirely different with his client.

When the client left I was invited in by Pa. "Bode," he said, "I dare say you smiled when you heard my voice." I could only smile again when I said, "I thought that you were addressing your client." He then repeated that what I was reading coincided with what his previous divination had revealed. With incredulity showing on my face Pa said, "Let me explain myself." He then told me the most astounding story (as I then thought) I had ever heard in my life.

"You must have forgotten that at the very beginning of time mankind came from Adamo (Adam), the father of all men. After the great flood, man then started to trace his new beginning from Noah, and that was why any man of good and proper behaviour amongst the Yoruba was, and still is, referred to as *omo-luwa-bi*, a corruption of *omo-Noah-bi*. It was after the flood that men, in their misguided wisdom, decided to build a tower which would reach up to heaven, so that if God decided to visit the earth with another flood they could all climb up to his abode. God came and inspected the tower, and then he made the common language in use at the time no longer intelligible to them; as a result they parted ways and scattered all over the face of the earth. From then until now men have worshipped that same 'almighty being' as each and everyone knew best. It was only those misguided ones, who did not believe in him, who failed to do so, as a result of which they denied the existence of their maker." Pa ended on this note: "Why do you think that the white priest sent you to learn from me?" He then asked, "Would you rather go to your Bible Class now, or listen to the story of Orunmila?" I opted to listen to him. So Pa Fagbemi continued.

* * *

A long time ago, before the *irunmales* (Yoruba gods) first visited Ile-Ife, an incident occurred in a village near Usi. Just before nightfall, an old man with white hair and a white flowing beard, dressed all in white, walked into the compound of the *Bale* (Head of the village). Although leaning heavily on a white walking stick, his sedate strides could best be described as majestic. He had a commanding presence with the appearance of a sage. On seeing him, the *Bale*, who was reclining on his couch, quickly got up to welcome the visitor. After having been offered a seat the old man introduced himself as Omo-Onire of Obameri, on the outskirts of Ile-Ife. He said that he had come to make a request from the *Bale*.

"*Alagba* (revered elder), what may that be?"

"My servants after a long and hard search reported

to me just this morning that this village would be the most suitable place for me and my sons to live."

"What is special about this small village, which gives it a preference to *Obameri* which is obviously a much larger village?"

"That exactly is the reason; *Obameri* is much too large for my youngest son."

"*Alagba*, please explain that to me."

"I have four sons; the youngest of them is a thinker."

"What do you mean a thinker?"

Right from the age of eight he started behaving as an adult. At six, when the neighbours started to call him *atikekere sogbon* (the young but wise one), at first I took no notice. By the time he was ten he started behaving like a wise old man! Often he would sit apart with a far-away look, like someone deep in thought; he seemed to be seeing things that we could not. Then he started using the voice of an adult. Again, as he didn't talk much, at first this went unnoticed. To hear him speaking, without actually seeing the speaker, you would think that you were hearing the voice of an old man! His wisdom and logic far exceeded his years. By the time he turned sixteen, which was about a month ago, he spoke with the wisdom of an older person. He was always seeking remote and quiet places for his meditation. It was then that I became convinced that there was something unique about him. So I asked my servants to seek a much smaller village with fewer people than in Obameri. It was reported to me only this morning that a small village surrounded by hills, sheltered and serene, had been found; they thought it was ideal. So I got here about two hours ago, along the side of the stream with the bamboo grove on its bank. Guided by one of my servants and one of your villagers who is his friend, I strolled around the entire village. I was struck by the peacefulness. I became convinced that they were right. Therefore I thought that I would seek your permission before I return home later this evening."

"If you don't mind me asking, what do you do for a living?" said the *Bale*.

"Have you ever heard of Ijana[6] palm oil?"

"Everyone knows about it."

"I own the forest where the oil is produced. The farm as well as the entire Ijana forests adjoining it have belonged to my family from time immemorial. I earn the best part of my income from both of them. In addition I breed ducks and pigeons, both of which

[6] I have often wondered if there is any connection between the name of Omo-onire's youngest son, Ajana and Ijana forest.

are known for their good quality. The climate here as well as your ponds will suit both the ducks and the pigeons."

Following this the *Bale* and the sage discussed a number of other things, presumably so as to know each other better. Intuition told the *Bale* that the coming of the sage would bring a lot of good to his village and to its people. Accordingly he granted the sage's request.

Two weeks after this initial visit, the sage and his four sons and other members of their families and servants arrived at the village. The *Bale* allocated them a large tract of fertile land towards the bamboo grove. Though the *Bale* had indicated that no payment was required, he took the money offered for the land, at the insistence of the sage. The sons of Omo-Onire who settled with him in the village were called: Oju-Ekun, *omo alara*; Arogbodo-Lewa, *omo ajero*; Gegelasa, *omo inu igbin kanko*; and Ajana.

The eldest son, Oju-Ekun, was a man of commerce with a great zest for the acquisition of money, wealth, and possessions. He was forever striving to become wealthier and wealthier. The second brother, Arogbodo Lewa, was a handsome playboy, too keen on the opposite sex, and as vain as *Okin*, the peacock. Gegelasa, the third one, popularly known as *Olomo Yindoyindo*, 'the one with an uncountable number of children,' was a great lover of kids. He was always looking for stray and neglected children so that he could cuddle and care for them. The youngest son was Ajana, the thinker. He was of a serious nature, and enjoyed conversing with old men. He was always seeking after knowledge. When he was not doing that he kept himself to himself.

When Omo-Onire had become old and frail, and thought that he was about to join his ancestors, he called his eldest son and said to him: "My child, I am about to be called home for my final rest. I have summoned you so that I can bless you with my *ase* (potent words), and so that you may ask for anything special you desire."

"Father, I wish to have wealth surpassing that of anyone else."

"Don't you think that you already have enough?" asked the old man.

"You asked for my wish and I have stated it."

His father blessed him confirming that his wish had been granted. The sage then sent for Arogbodo-Lewa. He posed the same question to him. He asked for beautiful women. "Don't you already have them to your heart's content?" the sage asked. "Father, you wanted to know my wish: I want women!" The father then asked if Arogbodo-Lewa was aware of the saying of the Yoruba elders that "a man who is overly fond of the opposite sex is likely to die by their hands."

"I am, and I'm willing to take the risk!"

The old man blessed him, adding that his wish had been granted.

The sage next sent for Gegelasa and repeated the same question. He asked for more children. He too was blessed and his wish granted.

When sent for, Ajana's request in reply to his father was this: "Father, my wish is to find the way that leads to *Olodumare*'s[7] abode, to enable me to offer him my services as his messenger, to interpret his messages to all men, so that the world may be made better."

His father was amazed: "What put that into your head?"

"I am certain that such a request will benefit all of mankind." The sage nodded, smiled and blessed him. He ended by saying, "My son, your wish has been granted." Not long after this, the sage died and was buried. He was mourned by the entire village.

[7] The supreme Yoruba God

In accordance with his wish Oju-Ekun became very wealthy. All kinds of people, from far and near came to borrow money from him. He accumulated many bondsmen[8] and extended his farms. Many of his debtors blessed and praised him while many others uttered *epe* (potent curses). No one was surprised when he died in his prime. In accordance with the prevailing custom, all his possessions – wives, wealth, children, and bondsmen – were divided into three equal parts and given to his three brothers. It is said that one of his descendants became the Oba Alara of Ilara Ekiti.

Similarly Arogbodo-Lewa was next to die due to the stress of his life with so many wives and concubines. All he possessed was divided in two, with equal portions going to each of his two remaining brothers. It is said that one of his descendants became Oba Ajero of Ijero Ekiti.

In due course, Gegelasa also died. The main cause of his death was the anxiety and strain of managing his countless children, biological, adopted, and inherited.

Now Ajana, the only surviving brother, had inherited all the possessions of his three deceased brothers: wealth, wives, children, bondsmen, and

[8] Tied workers who can only be released by paying back a "bond"

many other things. Ajana asked the messengers who brought the inheritance, the male children, as well as all the bondsmen, to build some huts, in fact as many as would be needed to house them all and to contain all the inheritance - hence the saying *Ajana olojule egbeje* (Ajana the possessor of 1400 huts). He released the bondsmen, and giving them farms and huts, liberating them, in fact. He allowed all the women to take husbands of their choice. From amongst the young men, he selected some who were willing to learn at his feet, and they became his pupils. And so he continued to think, and meditate, and to strive for peace and unity among all men. It was reported that after some time he disappeared from the village, which had increased enormously in size and wealth. Where he went no one knew, but he was greatly revered by all.

When the *irunmales* later paid their first visit to Ile-Ife, the place believed by the Yoruba to be the cradle of mankind, it was said that Ajana was one of them, now identified as Orunmila, god of wisdom and divination. He revealed the ways and wishes of Olodumare to men, through his divination. Among his names was *Elerin Ipin* (the one who witnesses the choice of destiny by each and every human being).

Comment

I was astounded by Pa Fagbemi's story, especially because of the features which seemed similar to Christianity. I was impressed that an old man of seventy-five could remember so vividly a tale he had originally been told forty-five years earlier and could recall it so well. There were no hesitations in his delivery, no faltering at all. When I asked for clarifications in some parts which appeared obscure, he gave me further explanations in an easy and candid way. His lucidity was impressive. I then asked for the secret of such a retentive memory and power of recall. He said that there were three main reasons for the quality of his memory. Firstly, he had understudied a very knowledgeable and experienced master, the *araba* of *Usi*, the most senior Ifa priest of the time, under whom he had served ten years, the last three as his *amu'gba legbe* (personal assistant). Secondly, he used the '*isoye*' provided by the *araba*. When I asked him what '*isoye*' was, he explained that it was a herbal preparation which aided retentive memory and the recall of information as and when required. He added that he was still using it. He gave me some, which

I accepted merely out of courtesy. In my ignorance, and due to my lack of faith, I later threw it away believing that I needed no aid to memory. Thirdly, he said that the *araba* who had told him the story of *Orunmila*, also taught him various formulae to aid retention and recall. Pa emphasised that the most important thing he had learnt from the *araba* was the need to remember the critical order of sequences; so, for example, in divination: who it was who came for divination; what was the purpose or cause; what Ifa revealed; what steps needed to be taken (usually these were sacrifices); what should be the types and nature of the sacrifices. Expressed in another way, the diviner, the one seeking divination, the purpose, the revelation, and the sacrifices prescribed.

Pa Fagbemi stressed that once you remembered the sequence, other things naturally fell into place. Here was a classic case of how high-level memorization functions within a primary oral culture. My own childhood training – for example, my father's requirement that I memorize songs from the traditional festivals such as Oro and Balufon– has helped me too to have a strong memory. In setting down the oral story which I have crafted into this written tale I did not need to refer to

my original report given to Canon King in June 1966
– except on one point, the name of the village near
Ife which Omo-Onire came from. In this way I hope I
have kept something of the original feeling of an oral
transmission through the generations.

The Similarities between Ifa and the Scriptures

I still find remarkable the references made by Pa
Fagbemi to various passages in the Bible. These
include Genesis 1:26 (The creation of man); Genesis
6:9–13 (Noah and the flood); and Genesis 11:1–9
(the tower of Babel). The central parable-like passage
in his story, where those concerned too much with
wealth, sex, and the preservation of their line, make
choices leading to their own disaster, finds many
echoes in the New Testament, notably, for example,
Matthew 6: 25–34, quoted above and which may
have provoked Pa Fagbemi to tell me the story, and
Galatians 5:10-26, which contrasts the fruits of the
spirit with those of the flesh.

I also find striking in the legend the emergence
of Ajana as Orunmila – that is to say, the good man
becoming a god. Clearly, these matters could only be

studied properly within the context of comparative religion and I do not have space to treat them fully here. They are part of my ongoing interest in oral culture, which I shall continue to research in this and related areas. In view of the ancient nature of Pa Fagbemi's oral story, passed down through many generations, I decided to give it the title "The Legend of Orunmila", though, as should now be clear, it could equally be called "The Parable of Orunmila."

THE EBIRIPO EPISODE

Introduction

We lived in Lagos, but while we were in the village during our holidays we stayed with our grandmother, who was called Iya-Agba. She was on her own since her husband, our grandfather, had died, except, of course, that she had servants and lots of relations staying with her.

We spent a lot of time with Granny in her kitchen which was in effect also her living room. One day we sat there watching her prepare the *dipon,* a mixture of beans and maize cooked with palm oil, which was to be taken to the *aro* – that is, a group or collective that helps with farm-work – for them to eat the next day.

Dupe, my cousin, was always asking questions. It was she who started the conversation about *ebiripo,* steamed grated cocoyam with palm oil and pepper.

"Grandmother," she began, "when we were at Ikenne yesterday we ate some delicious *ebiripo* which we enjoyed so much. I wanted to buy some more when we visited *okerobu,* the market-on-the-hill, today. You can imagine my surprise when the woman said: "You won't find it in Ogere market". Bunmi chipped in, thinking that they'd misunderstood something, but then another woman said, "It's taboo to sell *ebiripo* in the market or anywhere else in public in Ogere. Ask Granny when you get home. She'll back me up."

Grandma smiled saying that the woman was correct: "It is forbidden, and that has been the case since the *ebiripo* episode ages ago."

"Why is it forbidden here, especially when such a delicious food is freely sold in Ikenne and all over Remo?" asked Dupe. Grandma replied with a chuckle: "You children are fond of ferreting things out." The actual words used by Grandma in the Remo dialect were *"Ewven omode wve wven le topenpen urhun rhe nidi koko ju."*

"But Grandma, what's wrong to ask what everyone seems to know anyway?" retorted Dupe, clearly upset that she could not get an answer.

"Who says you have no right to know?" interjected the old woman. "I'm merely referring to your nosiness!"

"We don't normally live here; shouldn't we ask questions?"

"All right, I'll tell you," Grandma said. "All of you, come and sit down."

So Grandma started her story.

* * *

"Long, long ago Olipakala, an Ife prince, established Ogere[9] as a village by drawing together some smaller hamlets, sixteen in all. The new village encompassed Agbele, the largest of the hamlets, in the valley between it and what came to be known as Iperu, and other hamlets right up to Logorun, which then had its famous market lit at night by many earthenware lamps, and its outskirts went right up to the Ogun River. The story I am about to tell you arose from an event which happened about thirty years after the establishment of Ogere.

Ogere became well known for *esuru*, a type of yam common in the Remo area, which local people like to eat, and *afon*, African breadfruit, which is spherical in shape, about eighteen inches in diameter and weighs up to fifteen kilos. Its delicious cooked seeds were commonly eaten with a relish; it tastes good and is used for the prevention and cure of guinea-worms. The Ogere market also has its special rice ...

"What's special about Ogere's rice Grandma?" the

[9] An article in the *Punch* of Friday 16 October, 2009 (pp. 29–31) affirms that Ogere was established in 1401.

irrepressible Dupe interposed. "If you keep interrupting I shall not continue the story," Grandma said sternly. Dupe apologised and Grandma continued her tale.

The rice grown in Ogere farms has a special flavour which is equalled only by that in Ofada village, one of Ogere's neighbouring villages a few miles from here. The two villages have a special quality of soil that produces rice with a unique flavour. As a result, all and sundry flock to Ogere market for its rice as well as for its *afon*.

Suddenly our neighbours in Sinwun and Owode laid claim to the Ogere farms beyond Ogun and Edu rivers. At first, our ancestors thought it was a joke, but the incursions into the farms by the Sinwun farmers continued. On two occasions this led to serious confrontations. The intruders were met with so much force that they desisted for some time and Ogere thought that that was the end of the matter. But it was not so.

The last of the incidents almost turned into full-scale war. It took all the hunters and the entire troop of young Olopere warriors, the youths responsible for security and defence of the village, to repel the rapacious invaders. Again, it was thought that an end had been put to our neighbours' provocations.

Ten years after Olipakala had established Ogere, the tribesmen from the hills beyond Owode had sought an alliance with the Ogere warriors in order to repel some invaders from Idaomi, also known as Egun or Ajase, who wanted to take over Ota, an Egba settlement, with its large fields of sugar cane. A long war between the two factions resulted. So Ogunware, the foremost blacksmith in Ogere at that time, had to establish a new smithy at Ota for the on-the-spot fabrication of weapons of war. This earned him the nickname *agbede Ota ni ile onireke* meaning the eminent blacksmith of Ota in the land of sugar cane.

In fact Ogunware was a renowned hunter as well as a blacksmith. He was originally from Lagere in Ife. He was a member of the body that came over from Ijebu Ode to Ogere under the leadership of Olipakala, the founding father of Ogere. He was credited with establishing four smithies, in Lagere at Ife, in Ikoyi Ile, to the north of Ogbomoso, in Itunmaro in Ogere, and at Ota.

Shortly after this, the tribesmen from the hills, with the support of Ogere warriors, defeated the Idaomi invaders. With that victory the people of Ogere thought that all conflict had finally ceased, but unfortunately their neighbours at Sinwun and Owode were still hankering after the Ogere rice fields.

Some time after the Ota episode, the *Bale* of Owode sent an emissary to Alegunsen, the then Ologere (*oba*), to request assistance to repel the raiders from Idaomi who they claimed had again invaded the Papa farms just beyond Ofada. No one suspected that it was a ruse, as before then the Owode people had become seemingly friendly with the Ogere community. They bought most Ogere's production of *esuru* and *alo*, a type of yam, thin, yellowish in colour and slightly sweet in taste, which was as popular as the rice. What is more they paid higher prices than other buyers. Thus the Ogere people were lulled into a false sense of security. Alegunsen and his people heeded the call for help from the supposed friends against the Idaomi. A strong force of the Oloperes and hunters then left for Owode to give the required support.

Here Grandma paused to take a sip of water and to gauge the interest in the young people around her. They were sitting wide-eyed and impatient for her to continue the tale. Grandma took another slow sip of her water, and then continued.

* * *

The incident which is famous in our history took place a day before the annual Balufon festival and dance, for which all the maidens and other women had prepared for months. *Balufon* is the abbreviated form of *Obalufon*, the god considered to be the inventor of weaving and cloth. He is worshipped in Ijebu and Remo areas, and his favourite colour is purple.

Before the festival the women had consumed a lot of *awuje* (Lima beans) cooked with rich palm oil. They believed this made their skin shine for the public display which took place at the festival. The *balufon* drums had all been restrung and retuned; these are the special drums made with the skin of *ekiri*, wild goats. Male members of the four ruling houses of the new Ogere are the custodians of the drums.

The Ogere fighters left for Owode the day before the festival, much to the regret of both the warriors and the girls, for it was at this festival that partners were appraised and chosen for marriage. So the entire community was in something of a subdued mood.

All the women traders, with the exception of the greedy Efunbola, chose not to go to the Ajura market on the day of the Balufon. Efunbola was reluctant to miss the market and decided to slaughter four goats, instead of the usual two, to meet the demand created by the absence of her fellow traders. She and her niece, Ninse, were the only travellers going from Ogere to Ajura that morning. What enticed Ninse to accompany her was the tryst between her and her admirer from Lapoyo who was to meet her at Ajura. It was just as well she went! Had Ninse not gone to Lapoyo in search of her admirer (who had failed to show up at Ajura) the history of Ogere might have been very different. Some even say that Ogere might have been wiped out of existence.

A pleasant surprise awaited Efunbola at Ajura. Something that had never happened before, some strange men came and purchased her entire basket of *edenru* (roasted meat), much to the chagrin of her usual customers. When she asked others in the market who the men were, no one knew. All she was told was that they had arrived the night before, buying up everything and eating all the food in the town. Of course all the market women were pleased to make a lot of money off the strangers.

Efunbola was not complacent by nature and she was

highly sensitive. Her intuition told her that something was amiss, and shrewdly she asked her niece to enquire discreetly what was really going on. In the meantime she went to buy a few things to take home.

Ninse who had been racking her brains for excuses to sneak away to find her young admirer who had failed to turn up as arranged, was delighted. She said to herself cryptically, '*Awodi to nre bara, efufu ta ndi pe oni okuku muse ya*', ('the hawk that is Ibara bound is lifted at the tail by the wind; it says, now to business'). She was very pleased at the encouragement to do what she had wanted to do anyway. She went quickly on her way to Lapoyo village. She met her admirer who was cautiously leaving the village and asked him why he failed to meet her in Ajura.

He explained that the Bale of Lapoyo had banned all travel for two days, adding that it was with a great deal of difficulty that he had been able to escape his father's strict watch and leave the village. Ninse asked why such a ban should be imposed. He replied that, at first, he did not know exactly why but while eavesdropping the night before he had heard a neighbour telling his father that Ogere people were not to be told about the imminent invasion.

"Invasion?!" asked Ninse, with a terrified look. Her boyfriend then explained that apparently the Bale of the village had been given a huge bribe by the Owode chieftain to ensure that no one travelled to Ogere to warn them about the attack that had been planned. This was because Owode was aware of the friendly relationship between Lapoyo and Ogere. Lapoyo had the lion's share of the Ogere's rice in exchange for their palm oil.

Ninse's boyfriend then explained: "Besides, the Bale had assured the elders of Lapoyo that Owode soldiers could be easily defeated by the tough Ogere fighters. I was, however, dismayed when I later heard my father telling another neighbour that the Ogere warriors had been lured out of town. It was a carefully laid plan since there was no invasion by the Idaomi."

"What can we do?" asked the Ninse, very worried. "I don't know. Besides, it's rather late in the day and it will be dark soon," answered her boyfriend.

"That should not deter us; we must set out with all speed to Ogere immediately," countered Ninse. Thus the young lover had to run alongside Ninse. With the cunning of a hound, he suggested that they should keep to the forest in case the Ajura-Ogere footpath was

being watched. They both ran all the way to Oke-odo near Agbere before they stopped, out of sheer fatigue.

After a little rest they reached and crossed Joboyo stream as the sun was setting. In their effort to avoid being seen from the Ogun river end, they got into a large enclosed area where there was a thatched hut. With the crackling of the dried twigs and leaves the inhabitant of the hut heard their movement.

Out of the hut a woman's voice inquired, "Who are you who dare to approach this ground, sacred to Yemogun!" They were rooted to the spot. They could hear the snapping of twigs and leaves as a gaunt woman emerged. "This is forbidden ground, don't you know? Don't you see the *marigho* (palm frond) hanging up there? You are approaching a sacred grove. You are lucky I stopped you just in time; otherwise the goddess herself would have struck you dead," said the woman sternly.

Ninse was now shaking, and she fell at the woman's feet and held them in the manner of a suppliant. Both said to the woman, "Good mother, please help us to save Ogere."

"Save Ogere from what!?" asked the astonished keeper of the Yemogun grove. Ninse was still panting as she recounted what she had learnt, and her friend echoed her words. The old woman, whose initial anger had now calmed, invited them in and gave them cold water from an *amu* (a clay pot). She then asked them to repeat their story slowly. After hearing their remarkable tale again, she remarked: "My children, you must be right. Since this morning I have had the premonition of danger, especially when the wind suddenly started to howl, with all the birds hurtling and fluttering over the grove. To make matters worse, the dogs also joined in the howling; theirs were such blood-curdling howls, I wondered then what it could be. Now I know. Eat some *afon* and *eja-aro* (catfish) as you must be hungry.

Then I'll send you to the *Iyaloja* who, as you know, is the most powerful woman in Ogere."

Grandmother paused again to take a few sips of water. By this time, the children around her were desperate for her to continue with the exciting story.

After the two finished their meal, Grandmother told them, the old woman spoke almost in a whisper. "Listen carefully; go slowly and look cautiously left and right before you cross to the other side of the footpath to Mapagha. Do you know the house of Iyaloja? Go there. Show her this staff of office. Ask Iyaloja, and the Iyalode, the leaders of the elders, to come immediately. Tell her it is extremely urgent, but don't tell her what you have told me. Go. May Lipakala guard you both."

Fortunately the *Iyaloja* was at home, and she was not yet asleep. Before they knocked on the door, she had enquired who was approaching at such a late hour. She then peeped out carrying an earthenware lamp as it was already dark. "We have a message for you, respected Iyaloja, from the old woman at the grove. She gave us her staff of office to assure you that we come from her, and she told us to leave the staff with you. You and Iyalode Efuntolabo must go to see her tonight as soon as possible," they explained.

"The matter must be extremely important and urgent for her to entrust this ancient staff to such youthful hands as yours." Pointing to Ninse she said, "You must be a virgin, otherwise you could not have taken seven steps without having toppled over."

"Yes mama, I am."

"Who is your mother?"

"Moloko, of Maro compound," Ninse replied.

"*Ah Egbe mi* (a member of my age-group)" the old woman intoned. "Greet her for me. I hope to see her in the morning."

The entire village was thrown into turmoil to hear the *Oba*'s village crier at the first cockcrow clanging his gong with the metal bar. This was a clarion call, by the authority of the Ologere, to all women of Ogere, young and old. "Following this announcement you should all assemble promptly in front of the Iyaloja's residence. It is important and urgent that you all do so. Failure to comply will have terrible consequences." Within half an hour of this call the entire compound of Iyaloja was filled with the women, many of them without their head-ties *(idiku)*, but all with their *oja* firmly wrapped around their waists. They were surprised to be confronted not with Iyaloja alone, for beside her was Iyalode Efuntolabo, the *Jagun* of the foremost female *egbe*.

While they were still wondering what was so urgent, out of Iyaloja's front door stepped the *Yeye* herself, mother of the community, the *Alase* of Yemogun, decked in her purple *aso-oke*, a locally woven traditional dyed wrapper, over which was her white *oja* firmly in place, white *saki*, insignia of her position, and over her right shoulder a longish white horsetail fly-whisk with a handle covered in white beads. Another white *saki* was worn as a headdress over her white hair. She was clutching the *opa ase onide*, the ancient brass staff of her office, with the effigy of a dove as a handle. Though frail looking she was a sight to behold. Her unblinking eyes, which seemed to take in all that was around her, were shining. Her genial manner and comportment confirmed that she was indeed a high priestess. She was a sight to behold. Her presence was awe-inspiring.

Despite her gaunt frame, the *Yeye* exuded authority as the *Alase* of the revered goddess. A great hush fell when, before speaking, she raised her right hand, now holding the white fly-whisk. Her staff of office had been transferred to the left. Her sonorous voice vibrated with emotion, yet it was calm and clear as she spoke – so much so, that the old men looking from afar off could guess the meaning of her words, designed to urge and motivate, and to instil in the women the spirit of Yemogun. She ended on a note which all the women echoed: "Yes", they all shouted loudly, 'The one who supports us and never deserts us, Lipakala, will be with us. He will disgrace and defeat our enemies. Amen. Amen."- in the Remo dialect, *Lipakala, 'agbeni me dehin e te'ni nehin, e to owvon osika n'oju; wva ngha.* Soon after, they all dispersed in a jubilant mood.

The remaining menfolk in the village were inside their own compounds and the whole village was hushed. The atmosphere was charged. Suspense and an air of expectation hung in the air. The entire village was quiet except for Iya Ojuroye's compound where all the women had converged. The compound was as busy as a beehive. Some of the men and women, old and young, were busy peeling the skin off the coco-yams, others were busy grating them. Many women were engrossed wrapping the blended cocoyam in *aiba* leaves. Soon these were arranged into large earthenware pots. Underneath them were portable ovens consisting of pots with parts cut away for inserting firewood. The fires were blazing. Within the hour all the women except Ojuroye and Iyaloja had disappeared.

After an hour, the women were back with braided hair and smart purple wrappers and *oja* (waist bands). Later, they carried oval-shaped covered calabashes on their heads, and then filed in an orderly procession towards the Ogun river by way of the *panoda,* where paths crossed. There was a hush as they crossed the narrow bamboo bridge that spanned the Ogun River, coming down on the Oke-odo side. Soon many stalls appeared, manned by beautiful women, all decked in purple.

* * *

It was time for Grandmother to take another few sips of water, letting the tension rise among her attentive young audience. After what seemed an eternity to the children, while Grandmother coughed, patted her chest, and wiped her mouth, she continued her narrative.

At Owode as dawn broke it was quite a job waking up all the sleeping men, the group that had suddenly appeared the previous evening, Their leaders had to drag and kick them to get them up. Many were holding their heads in their hands. Several walked unsteadily until one of the leaders started splashing cold water on all of them, on their heads, faces and chests. The smell of *akara* (fried bean balls) and *moyinmoyin* (steamed blended beans wrapped in leaves), helped to complete the task of waking them.

They all descended on the food laid out on the grass beneath the trees. After eating, they started their military march. By the time they got around the Ajura bend leading straight to Ogere many of them were already tired. Oke asked if they had had breakfast. When some answered yes, he replied sharply, when? "Just now," he said, "but I feel empty. I need to eat some more." Most of them felt the same but were ashamed to admit it. The enormous quantities of goat pepper soup accompanied by *kekeye* (a strong alcoholic drink) that they had consumed so happily the night before had taken its inevitable toll on them. The *eko* (ground corn wrapped in leaves after steaming) and *akara* as well as the *moyinmoyin* served earlier that morning could not satisfy them.

By the time they reached the bridge at Agbere they were puffing and panting. The man leading the vanguard opened his eyes. He thought he was dreaming. Right in front of them were stalls behind which were pretty women unwrapping what looked like *ekuru* (steamed ground beans without oil) but with a more pleasing aroma. Whatever it was, it had an unusually arresting and enticing smell. *Oke abolonjeku*, 'Guzzle Guts' himself, the front man, was the first to taste the delicious *ebiripo*. "We have reached the abode of the dwellers of the enchanted vale," he yelled. "Come and eat," he encouraged the others. The entire body of men went scrambling for the *ebiripo*. When they had satisfied themselves they became exceedingly thirsty. In one mad rush they made for the River Ogun. Down they went on their knees and bellies, lapping at the water. They were all so mad with thirst that those behind surged forward in a frenzied haste to reach the water as well. Thus they trampled over those in front. As they all drank, some slid forward, others slid straight into the river, yet others were pushed into it from the rear by their comrades who were desperate to satisfy their thirst.

It was a scene of utter chaos. Then came a hush. The resulting quiet was indescribable. The remaining few in the rear looked on mesmerized. It was as if they were in a trance. Though they had the urge to flee, their legs seemed like lead. Amidst the confusion, like men dreaming, they saw more beautiful women – to some of them, it was like a hallucination – emerging from the bushes around them, urging them to eat and refresh themselves. The scent of the tempting food was like something from outside the world of mortals. Completely mesmerised, they fell on the neatly folded parcels of food, now being unwrapped by the shapely hands of the women whose smiling faces enticed them to eat more.

Having eaten their fill, like those who are possessed, they all made their way towards the river, causing yet another stampede and confusion. They were, however, hampered by the piles of bodies that had previously been trampled on and who lay dead or dying in front of them in all kinds of strange postures. They stumbled over these bodies. All too soon there came a great hush, like the silence of the grave. The much-anticipated battle never took place. Instead the attacking force was defeated by those who are sometimes described as the weaker sex. The women had won the day. So ended the *ebiripo* episode, with the complete rout of the invaders.

Thus came true, though with a twist, the saying of the Yoruba elders, *b'okurin ri ejo ti obirin pa a; ani k'ejo sa ti ku*, meaning 'what does it matter if a man is first to see the snake which is later killed by the woman', an expression usually used for cowardly males, though that was certainly was not the case on this occasion. What mattered, in this critical instance, was that Ogere was saved.

Some said that Yemogun, the revered wife of *Olipakala* herself, had appeared to inspire the women. To commemorate this momentous event the *Oba* and *Igbimo* of Ogere forbade from that time on the public sale in Ogere of *ebiripo*, the fatal food that had saved Ogere and its people. The ban remains in force, from that day to this.

THE KING'S GATEKEEPER

There was a well-known market in the domain of Oba Wasere which was popularly known as Ilu Idera. Idera market, right in the centre of the town, was large and offered an extensive variety of the goods. The local inhabitants, however, fondly called their market *'emi Idera'* meaning the heart of Idera community, which it was indeed, as everything, except the *oba's* palace, revolved around it. It was not merely a place for commerce, it was also a centre for local entertainments, with its *sakara*, *alugba* and *ogidigbo* forms of music. It was great fun to listen to and dance to these melodious tunes in the evenings. It soothed the nerves, made you forget your worries and gave you new energy.

Idera was also famous for its stilt dancers and acrobats. It was also the place to exchange news and disseminate information, especially about foreign and distant lands. The section of the market for *aso oke* – the locally woven and dyed cloth – as well as for rams and goats, was the most popular in the entire district. Idera was indeed the heart and centre of Idera township.

Oba Wasere, whose full name was Awaye Wasere (meaning one sent into the world to make it better) was a very popular monarch. He was widely known for his generosity and geniality and greatly revered. He wished everyone within his domain to be happy and contented. He had what is generally referred to as open arms and an open heart. It delighted him no end to receive and entertain his subjects as well as strangers.

Anyone who wanted to see the King, no matter how lowly, was allowed to do so, provided whoever it was came at the prescribed time and was willing to wait, no matter how long it took. One other attraction was that no visitor, no matter how humble, left the palace without a gift.

This generous practice by Oba Wasere was considered strange, because it was contrary to the practice at that time among other *obas*, who believed in and followed to the letter the old custom of kings receiving presents, so as to induce favours. This practice was once referred to as *somi, somi la ngbo n'ile oba*, meaning 'help me off-load from my head the present for *kabiyesi* (his majesty)'.

Unsurprisingly, the king's gatekeeper was always kept busy and he enjoyed his role tremendously. Nite, the gatekeeper, was a law unto himself. Nobody, except the high and mighty, was allowed into the palace without a solemn promise that at least one tenth of whatever was received from the king, or its equivalent in cash, would be passed on to him.

Almost everyone knew about this obnoxious practice, yet they all condoned it, as they would want to come back, again and again, to a warm welcome from Nite. So they all submitted to his odious ways; no one wanted to bell the cat! Although the gatekeeper's real name was not Nite, his unpleasant character had earned him, from the populace, this notorious nickname deriving from *Alainitelorun*, one who was never contented. The number and weight of curses heaped on Nite daily can be imagined.

One day, a man named Nimbe – whose full name was Olorunmbe, (God exists) visited the palace. As usual he promised a tenth of whatever present he got from the King to the gatekeeper. Nimbe was a very poor peasant who lived a long distance from the palace. He walked with a limp that made the long distance difficult and tiring for him. As a result, he visited the King only once a year. Aware of his circumstance, the King was always more generous with him. In addition to money the King would give him food such as yams, corn and fruit. On this occasion as in the past Nite took his share of the king's largesse.

Nimbe eventually got home after a very exhausting journey to and from the palace completely exhausted. His friend and neighbour, Alatunse (meaning he who makes amends) helped him to unload his basket and to put its contents inside his hut. While doing so Alatunse observed the odd number of yams and other items. There were only three yam tubers and eighteen oranges. Also a few bananas were missing from the bunch. On asking how this came about Nimbe explained that it was due to the 'toll' exacted by Nite.

The following week Alatunse decided to visit the King's palace. On arrival at the palace Nite exacted from Alatunse the usual promise of payment. Alatunse, as customary, was received graciously by the King. When he was leaving the King asked him what he would like as a present out of the range of gifts on offer.

"None of these" he said.

"What is it then you wish for?" asked the King.

"Twenty strokes of the cane," he said.

"That's odd" observed the King. "May I ask why?" he added.

Alatunse then explained the bargain between him and Nite. The King was astounded and furious. He, the benevolent monarch, could not believe that such a dastardly practice of extortion could be happening within his domain, let alone in his palace

He then admonished everyone present, adding, 'Did not our elders say *Bi ara ile eni ba nje kokoro buruku, ti a ko so fun, huruhere e ko ni i je ka sun loru,* which means if a member of one's household is eating bad insects and is not cautioned, his or her hacking cough will not permit one any sleep during the night'. If you do not advise your brother you will share in his misfortune.

With righteous indignation the King ordered Nite to be brought immediately before him. When questioned by the courtiers and confronted by Alatunse, he confessed. "How long has this practice been going on?" asked the King. All those present within the King's audience room chorused that the practice had existed for as long as Nite had been the gatekeeper.

The King was exceedingly sad to hear it. He then asked for one of the guards to be called in to administer the flogging; not on Alatunse but on Nite and not twenty strokes but twice as many. In addition Nite was immediately sacked as gatekeeper and banished from the King's domain. Alatunse was highly commended for bringing Nite's corrupt practices to the attention of the King. He was also presented with very handsome gifts. In making the presentation the King's chief Counsellor said:

"This incident has reaffirmed the truth of the Yoruba saying *'ijo gbogbo ni t'ole; ijo kan ni ti onihun'*, which means 'whereas its every day for the thief the owner has only one, the day of reckoning, which is both important and salutary. You have indeed lived up to your good name, Alatunse (he who makes amends). May many others in this land emulate your conduct."

THE QUEST FOR THE RARE LEAF

AND OTHER YORUBA TALES

THE THIEF AND THE WHITE CHIEF

Oganla village with its hills and valleys is very picturesque. You can approach the village from different directions but the main route from its nearest neighbouring village, Ipele, is by far the most beautiful. Coming from Ipele one has to descend into the valley before climbing a very high hill to enter Oganla The ancient trees on both sides of the rough stony road cast their leafy branches over the entire stretch forming a shaded tunnel. A tired visitor would be tempted to sit beneath one of the trees to take a rest before entering the village. This haven of peace is one of the many attractions which make Oganla a well loved place.

Many of the men in the village are farmers but there are also a few traders and craftsmen: blacksmiths, masons, bricklayers, carpenters and wood carvers. The village has one famous gold- and silversmith and also a second-hand clothes dealer, who is a very popular man. He is jocularly referred to as the friend of Kasali, who is one of the most flamboyant and popular characters in Oganla. Tall, handsome, and amiable, Kasali is liked by all, especially by the opposite sex.

Many of the women in the village are housewives.

Those of them who carry on one trade or another usually do so from home. By far the most popular trade is cooking and selling food such as rice, *dipon* (a mixture of beans and corn cooked with palm oil), *moyinmoyin* (steamed blended beans with palm oil wrapped in leaves), *amala* (steamed yam flour), pounded yam, *ogi* (pounded maize soaked in water prior to being made into paste) and *awuje* which is made from lima beans.

Oganla is a very lively and happy village. With its rapid development it is on the verge of becoming a town. It hosts many festivals: *oro* which some say is an *orisa* (a god) - *oro*, the roaring bull which makes its loud voice heard by all. In ancient times its worshippers formed a guild called *osugbo*. There is also the *Agemo* or *Agemon*; this is also an *orisa* worshipped mainly in Ijebu and Remo. Its worshippers are known as Alagemo. *Agemo* is a cult performed in secret and hidden from women. Also popular are Eluku (a type of masquerade) and Balufon, or Obalufon, the name of the god who is considered to be the inventor of clothing and the art of weaving; and *Egungun*, a masquerade which is also well-liked and is generally considered to be the reincarnated spirit of an ancestor. Its dress is *ago* (an especially decorated costume which is a great work of art) and it has an unnatural accentuated voice. Another thrilling masquerade which is equally admired is *asa* which is peculiar to Remo; it is called *agere* in other Yoruba towns and villages. The performer walks or even dances on stilts, a pair of upright poles with supports for the feet, high above the ground.

Kasali is very sociable. Everybody, young and old, is fond of him and likes his company. Like most of the men he works on his farm in the mornings. In the evenings he is to be seen with a *sakara* musical group. He is equally as good with the drums and on the *agidigbo*. In between singing, dancing and generally entertaining those around he regales the company with stories. He is well known for his numerous jokes and banter. In spite of all his good points everyone knows that Kasali is a thief, indeed, an experienced and clever rogue. Some refer to him as a professional thief. It is generally believed that he has a special *juju* that aids him. One good thing about him is that he never steals from Oganla. He always brings his 'goodies' from other towns and villages. He has a handful of assistants who are euphemistically referred to as his 'apprentices'. They are ardent students in the art of thievery.

It is in the lively setting described above that Kasali

and his band operate. Kasali is indeed an extraordinary rogue. If one were to write about all his exploits, it would fill many books; it suffices to recount only two of them here.

Oganla boasts of four churches, or 'missions' as they were known locally in the old days. Of course, the worship of the many indigenous *irunmales* is still widely prevalent. Yet, remarkably, adherents of the various religions mix and interact together cordially. Oganla might be described as a most tolerant and harmonious community.

One of Oganla's missions has a white minister who has lived in the area for over three decades. He was honoured with title of chief by the paramount ruler of the district many years earlier. His residence is about seven miles away from Oganla, and he is also responsible for the entire district comprising of more than thirty towns and villages. Friendly and well known to all, he is generally referred to as the 'white chief'. He is an eloquent speaker and is fluent in Yoruba; thus he has a great rapport with the people.

The white chief and Kasali met some time ago at one of the social gatherings at the mission house. Although Kasali is not a Christian, he is very sociable and generally participates in the mission's social functions. The mission maintains an open door policy in the hope of making new converts. During a conversation between the two men, the priest jokingly referred to Kasali's reputation.

"I am intrigued by the powers attributed to your unique *juju*," the white chief remarked.

"Do you believe the stories?" asked Kasali.

"You may fool simple folks with such tales, but a man of God like me cannot be intimidated or impressed by them," the white chief affirmed.

"So why don't we put it to the test?" asked Kasali.

"How?"

"I can come and operate in your mission house for instance."

"You will fail if you try."

Kasali assured him that he will 'visit' him shortly.

The mission yard in which the white chief lives is by far the largest in the area. This is understandable as it is the district headquarters of the mission. In addition to the chapel, which the local inhabitants call the 'prayer house', it has many other buildings such as the school house, the mission offices, private residences for the teachers and church workers as well as a clinic. The entire mission compound has high brick walls. At night, guards are always on duty. By local standards, the compound is considered impregnable. Apart from the chapel, the residence of the white chief is the most prominent. It is a large brick and timber structure with, various offices and meeting rooms on the ground floor and living rooms and bedrooms on the first floor. The rooms with balconies are spacious and look out on the many tall trees in the compound.

One Friday night, Kasali decides to pay the white chief a visit. It is a dark and moonless night. It is a particularly cool night and all the good people within the mission yard are enjoying the sleep of the just. Kasali has no difficulty in gaining entrance into the yard. Having been to the clinic on several occasions, he knows the compound well. Quietly he climbs one of the tall trees that surround the white chief's residence. In no time he quietly lets himself down onto the chief's bedroom's balcony. As the windows are all wide open, he has no difficulty in making an entry.

The white chief is asleep on his comfortable bed covered by a mosquito net. Beside him is a coffee table on which are various bibles, hymnals and other books. His spectacles are lying on the open bible. Beside it is

his favourite pocket watch as well as his wallet. After looking round Kasali decides to take the spectacles, pocket watch and a Bible. He quietly leaves the room through the window by which he gained entry. Using the tree again, he climbs over the fence and melts into the night.

When the white chief wakes up in the morning his pocket watch and spectacles are missing as well as the Bible he was reading before he fell asleep. He wonders if they are in the study on the ground floor and, just as he is about to call his housekeeper, his servant appears at the door to announce a visitor. "At this hour of the day? Who is he? Has he been here before?" asks the white chief. Getting no satisfactory reply from the

121

servant, he decides to go downstairs to investigate. There he finds Kasali, calmly sitting. As the white chief enters, Kasali rises and greets him respectfully.

Since the day of their last conversation the white chief had not given Kasali any thought. "This is a great surprise," says the white chief in response, "and to what do I owe the honour of this visit?"

"I am here, white chief, to enquire after your health and to return to you some property of yours."

Thereupon Kasali brings out from the deep pocket of his *agbada* (robe) a pair of spectacles, the pocket watch and the Bible.

"How did you find them?" the white chief asks.

"I removed them last night when I paid the visit I promised you when we last met. As I did not call professionally, I did not take your wallet which was on the table. What I did, I did for the fun of it and to prove to you, white chief, that the gods of our people are still powerful."

The white chief looks at Kasali in disbelief. "You were actually in my bedroom last night and I did not wake up?" stammers the white chief.

"If there had been one hundred of you in the room I would have entered unseen. White men do not possess all the powers," Kasali responds with bravado.

"Please pardon my ignorance," the white chief replies with a wry smile. The two shake hands and Kasali leaves.

Later that afternoon the white chief recounts the episode to the *Babaijo*, the lay president of a nearby church. He asks him what he thinks of the incident. The *Babaijo* replies promptly. "Kasali is the best of them all. He is widely known in these parts and beyond. We must thank God that he is your friend, as it will not do to have him as an enemy. All the white chief could do is mutter, "We live and learn".

———◆—

KASALI STRIKES AGAIN

Baba Akin was the *Olorode*, chief and head of the hunters, of Igbehinadun district as his father had been before him. He was very tall and fair-skinned. He had great presence and was highly respected. Usually, the hunters would congregate at his compound in the early evenings about the time the night market began. They discussed matters of common interest. Such gatherings would break up about the time the night market was closing. This was to enable those going on night-hunting to be well fed by their wives.

One night after the hunters had left, my companions and I who were home on holiday decided to visit the *Olorode* who was my late mother's eldest brother. The visit was partly because of the bush meat which visitors were offered in his compound which we city dwellers enjoy eating, and partly to be entertained by his enthralling stories. When we got there Kasali and another man were with the *Olorode*. Soon after our arrival, however, Kasali and his companion left. I supposed this was to enable us enjoy the company of the old man undisturbed. As Kasali was leaving my uncle deliberately wiggled his nose and said *'sio'*, a word and gesticulation commonly used in the locality to show disdain; but this apparent disrespect, in this instance, seemed to show a trace of admiration. We thought that this was funny and puzzling. Needless to say, we made no comment.

A few minutes after this, Sanya asked if the old man who had just departed was the notorious thief, Kasali. My uncle nodded. "Is he as clever and as dangerous as was widely reported?" I asked.

"Very much so," answered my uncle. "Why is he different from all the other robbers?" I again asked.

"He relies on the *ofo* and *ogede* (incantations) he learnt from his late father, Bamise, who was in my age group. He was the leading herbalist in this area. Kasali worked under him as an apprentice for many years and he learnt a lot from him. Kasali has more knowledge of spells and charms than most people in these parts.

"What exactly are *ofo* and *ogede*?" I enquired. "They are potent words inherited from our ancestors who used them in warfare and for hunting. When used their opponents would be reduced to near idiots or would just lie down and sleep; sometimes ferocious animals have been known to have cowered or suddenly developed lockjaw or have their claws broken at crucial moments just before being attacked," my uncle explained.

"Did that really happen?" I asked incredulously. "Of course, I know and have used the *ogede* and *ofo* myself. How do you think I succeeded as the best hunter for years before being elevated to the position of *Olorode*?"

"Please tell us about Kasali. We want to know whether or not the stories about him were exaggerated," I entreated.

"Have you heard an account of his last operation, before he disbanded his gang?" asked my uncle. We all said 'no'. "That was an interesting episode," the old man said.

He then went on: "Years ago in the days of Eleku, your paternal grandfather, there was a bold robber, a stranger, who lived in Oganla village. Where he came from no-one knew. He was charming and extremely pleasant. He was very popular because of his cordial relationship with everyone. The elders say '*awolu mate o mo won ara re ni*' (a stranger who behaves will not be disgraced). Kasali was his foremost assistant. He taught Kasali many things until he too became a master thief. The powers he had acquired from his father added to Kasali's cleverness as a professional master thief. He had a number of assistants, euphemistically called apprentices. As everyone knew, Kasali was and still is a musician. He plays the *agidigbo,* and he is one of the best at *sakara* (a form of Yoruba dance and music). Up till now he is still the leader of a s*akara* band. He played most evenings at the night market, which he still does. When dancing had ceased late in the evening he would switch to his main business which normally began about midnight. He chose teams for operations at random from his band of 'apprentices'. None of them ever had more than a few hours' warning before any operation. He did all the spade work and planning himself. One good thing about Kasali was that he never operated in Oganla. His philosophy was *'ka ma ko ere oko wale',* bring the good things from elsewhere to Oganla.

Before any operations Kasali usually made a good study of his victims: the house and the area in which they lived as well as what they had by way of possessions. The *Balogun*[10] of Idi-Isin had for some time been high on his list of intended victims. This was because of his wealth: his collection of *aso-oke,* other rare costumes, and rare valuable ornaments; besides, his assortment of gold and coral beads was one of the best in the district. As previously mentioned Kasali did not warn members of the gang and he varied the

[10] Although now used for the head of a society or a body, the title is strictly that of a commander of the veteran warriors.

selection of members for each operation. In the case of the intended onslaught against the *Balogun* of Idi-Isin, he selected only four from the gang. They were informed only on the morning of the operation. They were asked to assemble at the market place early in the evening. Between then and nine they sat at the palm-wine bar drinking. As an *agidigbo* band was in attendance they did some dancing. They also enjoyed the bush meat for which the bar was popular. As most of the market women started to leave for their homes two members of the gang left the bar. A little later the other two departed. Kasali waited for another fifteen minutes before he sauntered out after them. Their rendezvous was the dreaded *Igbo-obi* (the forest of kola nuts, a notorious spot) where three roads met down in the valley between Oganla and Ipele. From there they walked briskly past Ipele village towards Idi-Isin town. Just before the main entrance to Idi-Isin they made a detour. It was at this juncture that Kasali told the gang the target for the night's operation. Although the *Balogun*'s house was near the market a small cluster of trees separated the market and his compound.

Two members of the gang acted as look-out men. Kasali himself was accompanied by the other two.

It was a dark and windy night. It was misty and it had started to drizzle There were no stars in the sky; neither was there any sign of the moon.. Just the perfect conditions for this operation, thought Kasali. They scouted around the area to check on the movements of the many *asode*, the night watchmen. Only after that the operation commenced. Kasali helped himself to a tall ladder from the nearby sawmill. He then instructed a member of the gang to hold the ladder firmly against the high wall. The other followed Kasali up the ladder. At a point Kasali signalled for him to stop. The gang member had the two large sacks which had been brought for the operation. Kasali clambered silently up to the roof and dropped down, similarly noiselessly, into the courtyard. At this point he stood still, gently inclined his head and started to whisper one of his most potent *ogede*: ... he ended on the note,

Asun fonfon n'tifon;
Asun mapa'rada niti igi aja;
Gbogbo eni ti owa ninu ile yi e sun;
Mo ni k'e sun.

(All those in this abode go into deep sleep like the beams of a roof.)

He then took a small gourd of charms from his

pocket and tipped a small quantity of its contents onto his left palm; this he blew into the air. He then proceeded cautiously. Obviously he knew his way around. He went through passages treading very quietly like a cat. Eventually he reappeared at a window, just above where his assistant was stationed. He signalled him to be at the ready. About fifteen minutes later he let down the first big *agbada* (the largest Yoruba outer robe). It was soon followed by the matching *dansiki* (tunic) and pair of *sokoto* (trousers), *aso ibora* (wrapper) and embroidered *fila* (decorated cap). Others followed in rapid succession. This went on for about forty minutes until all the targeted pieces had been passed down.

The operation was completed without any hitch and the party departed without any interruption. On getting back to base Kasali asked his men to produce the loot. He then discovered that the best pieces were missing. "How come? I personally lifted and passed on the various items including the special ones down to you," he said, pointing to the assistant stationed on the ladder. "I, therefore, should know what was lifted," he continued. To be absolutely certain he again enquired, enumerating one by one the items passed down:

The set of *alare* (scarlet coloured *aso oke*).

'Not there' was the answer.

The *Etu* (navy blue *aso oke*),

Not there.

The *Sanyan* (beige *aso oke*),

Not there.

The light damask.

Not there.

Dandogo eleya (the large pleated robe),

Not there.

Where is the package containing the gold and coral beads chains?

Not there.

They all looked at one another in bewilderment. Completely exasperated, Kasali left them in a huff. The following morning he summoned all members of the gang, including those who did not participate in this operation. He recounted to all present what had happened the previous night. He ended by asking if anyone had a change of mind. Still there was no reply. Kasali then said "I will give you one more day to rethink. If there has been no development by the end of tomorrow, every member of the gang is to report at the usual rendezvous for important meetings, first thing in the morning, the day after tomorrow, about the time farmers depart for their farms."

Kasali received no further report on the following day. So, on the appointed day everybody reported at the usual meeting-place. Then Kasali threw the bombshell.

"*Ogbon ki i tan l'aye ka wa lo s'orun*", that is, the world is not so bereft of wisdom to warrant a trip to heaven. The testimony of the owner is crucial; we shall all now proceed to Idi Isin to pay the *Balogun* himself a visit. This will give him the opportunity to confirm the things removed from his residence on the day of the incident."

There was utter silence. Then one member of the gang, visibly shaking like one having the ague, asked with temerity, "Master, you mean we will ask the owner himself what items of clothing and other valuables were stolen from his house?" "That's precisely what I have in mind", answered Kasali. The member now perspiring profusely further interjected with shaking voice, "How could we do that without giving ourselves away?" Promptly Kasali answered, "At this stage it is essential we obtain the testimony of the owner unless you have an alternative suggestion." He went on further "*Bi omode ba gbongbon kiku iya re a gbongbon sin sin re.*" This means if a child has the wisdom to die, the mother will find the enlightenment to bury it. All they could do was to look askance at one another. Had it been possible to read minds, a lot would have been discovered within the breasts of the individual members as they marched steadily towards Idi Isin. Unfortunately none had such a gift.

So they proceeded towards Idi Isin; members of the gang still thought that the master was bluffing. On they went, going via Igbo-obi and past Ipele. As they approached Idi Isin, all of them with the exception of Kasali, started to fidget. Kasali made a beeline for the Balogun's residence without a backward glance, passing through the cluster of trees. He knocked loudly on the main door. When it was opened by one of the servants, he greeted the man cheerfully and told him that members of the Oganla community had come to pay their respects to the *Balogun* in order to commiserate with him for his recent loss. The *Balogun* was a member of the Moslem community in Oganla and had sometimes led the Friday *Jumat* prayers. It was, therefore, no surprise that they came to sympathise with him. They were duly conducted to the *Balogun*. To greet him they all prostrated themselves before him with respect for his age and standing in the community.

Kasali then said that he and his colleagues learnt that the *Balogun* had been visited by robbers. When the *Balogun* said that this was so, he gave the customary greeting suitable for the occasion:

May you live long.

Your loss has purchased

for you lengthy life.

The owner will continue to have,

while the thief will never

gather enough to become wealthy.

The Balogun thanked them profusely. Kasali then said, "I hope that magnificent damask robe you used at the last Ramadan festival was not taken."

"It was." "Good gracious; I hope they overlooked the *Alare* – the scarlet coloured outfit."

"Of course not."

"My goodness, that irreplaceable garment. Let's thank God, you still have the native woven gown."

"Who says? That was taken as well."

"With the navy and beige robes you still have you will be able to manage until the stolen ones are replaced."

"My dear young man, they made a clean sweep; all is gone, including my favourite velvet pleated robe which I used on the occasion of my last visit to you."

"Good heavens; they must be a hard hearted gang."

After a few minutes more and following another prayer said by Kasali they left the Balogun's house. They were all uneasy as they filed out silently from the compound. Hardly had they gone twenty yards when Kasali repeated the words of the Yoruba elders: '*Bi yio bale bi yo bale ni labalaba fi nwogbo lo: ara aibale ni t'awodi*' (It would land if the way a butterfly would fly into the bush; restlessness is the lot of the eagle). Everyone remained silent. They were at the main entrance into the village when Kasali asked them all to come to their usual meeting place. When they had all arrived Kasali cleared his throat. He then said, "In the past we all believed that *agbajo owo la a fi nsoya*, (unity is strength}. But going by recent developments things seem to have changed; it appears now that it is now everyone for himself. There is no doubt that *ni isenyin ba'se je ti wo arin wa; igi woroko ti i nda'na ru* (at present we have in our midst someone who is like a crooked piece of stick which scatters the fire, just as an evil person spoils a feast). As you all know *ti awo ko ba gbe awo ni igunpa, awo a te* - if members of a cult are not supportive of one another the cult will crash. Our elders also say '*ki oju ma ri ibi ese l'ogun re'* (for the eyes to see no evil, the legs are the medicine). Medicine as used here is like a talisman. The meaning of this last proverb is that the legs bear the responsibility of transporting the eyes (and its owners) away from locations that might harbour evil. My advice is that you should all leave this village before cockcrow tomorrow; of course, none of you will dare to return until after my death".

One of them replied, "I am sure, highly respected master, that the guilty ones have already become wise. I am in no doubt that by nightfall all the garments and other valuables will be returned to you."

On this note Kasali left them and went to the palm-wine joint to cool off. On getting home later that night his most junior wife was waiting on the front veranda. She reported that three of the boys had been and left three bags. "These two," she said pointing, "are the missing things. They are returned with profuse apologies. The third one contains the *itaran ati owo ngbe nde agba,* a self imposed fine for the inconvenience caused to an elder.

A few days after the events related above Baba Akin went to his *etile* farm, which is a farm near the village. On entry into the farm he at first thought that he was in the wrong farm, but on looking up, the four *ose* (baobab) trees, the boundary markers, were still in place, and so were the newly planted *serigu*[11] fences. All the same he wondered; who or what could have weeded the farm, straightened the pathways between the mounds and replaced the canes for the yam tendrils. All his children and grandchildren were busy on their own farms and he no longer had farm workers. He walked to the barn. As he was about to sit down he thought that he heard a movement in the attic. Yes, there it was again.

"Who is there?" he asked. "It is me, Deru, Baba."

"Deru, what on earth are you doing here? Your old mother has been frantically looking for you." As he was speaking Deru came down the ladder which had been let down through the hatch. After prostrating himself to greet Baba Akin, the young man squatted and said, "When Kasali disbanded the gang, he gave us until the following morning to leave the village. As I had no other place to go I went into my mother's store, took four tubers of yam, a bunch of plantain and a small keg of palm-oil and came here. I had been praying and hoping that you would come. Thank God you are now here, *Baba*, what do I do?"

Sit down and tell me what happened, the whole

---

[11] Serigu is a Remo word for *botuje* – a Yoruba word. In full it is *olobotuje* = *ewe ayaba* = *lapalapa* (Jatropha Curcus). It is also called ringworm because the oil causes irritation on the skin of the children.

story." When Deru had completed his story Baba Akin assured him that he would intercede with Kasali to allow him to continue to live in the village, which he did. Since then Deru has become my retainer. He works on my farm and he is very well paid. That was the young fellow you saw with Kasali earlier this evening. He now plays with Kasali's *sakara* band. The *Olorode* ended by saying "*Ore kikikiti, iyekan katakata, ijo ore kitikiti ba ku iyekan katakata ni yio gbe sin*" which is, Deru and Kasali are now hand in glove, only death will separate them.

WHAT COMES AFTER SIX?

Driving into Oganla from Ipele I noticed an imposing new building at the top of the rocky hill. I wondered when it was built. Fortunately my cousin, Labajo, the current *Olorode* of Oganla was sitting beside me. When I pointed to the building asking who built it and when, he told me that it had been built about seven years earlier by Tunde, the son of one Lanuyi, now deceased, who was a contemporary of Teacher Taiwo, his late younger brother. I noticed that while speaking his face had a tell-tale expression. This provoked me to ask him to tell me all about Lanuyi's son, Tunde, when we got home.

Later that evening, as we sat with Sanya and two others by the barbecue, cousin Labajo told the interesting story of late Lanuyi's family. Lanuyi, an only child, lived in the village, where he had his primary education. As he did not attend the middle school, he did not have enough qualifications to be a pupil teacher, which was the employment to which most young people of his time resorted to in and around the village. Although he had the elementary rudiments of farming, he did not know enough to make a living out of it, nor was he inclined to take agriculture as a career;

but having had the good fortune to inherit his father's farm and house, he reluctantly took up farming. He gradually discovered that farming was not as dull as he had once thought. For the first time, he became aware of the pristine beauty of the forests and trees; the singing birds, especially the distinctive song of the Senegal dove, or laughing dove, which the locals call *oderee koko*; the meandering rivers which shimmer in the sunlight; the squirrels darting here and there; and the fresh smell of the forest. He also grew to appreciate the clean, cool and fresh air; the beautiful blue sky peeping through the huge ancient trees; and the shrubs and hedges tinted with all sorts of colours. With such beautiful scenery confronting him day in and day out, Lanuyi felt contented with his lot at least for the time being.

Relying on his meagre income from farming and his late father's goodwill he got married to a woman from the village. They had two children, a boy and a girl. As the children grew older, however, he found that his income could not sustain the family, let alone educate the children. So he decided to do what some of his friends had done before him, leave the village for Lagos to make his fortune. He was lucky to find employment there with a good master, an ex-serviceman who had started a business with his discharge pay. He was in the business of selling building materials and ironmongery. During his apprenticeship, Lanuyi was given a room in the master's house and a small allowance, the greater part of which he sent to his family back in the village each month. He was able to visit the village once every three months. He learnt his new job quickly and was soon promoted to the position of salesman and was now able to earn a commission in addition to his small salary.

He was so good at communicating with people in a friendly way that he started to make good sales that earned him sizeable commissions. He saved much of his earnings since he lived frugally. Soon, he became a sub-distributor and moved to the outskirts of Lagos, to serve those who would find it difficult to travel on the poor roads into the city. In addition, many dreaded the turmoil and crowds in Lagos. Besides, the outskirts provided better and cleaner accommodation, costing less than the high rents charged by the unscrupulous landlords of Lagos.

Before long, his business grew to such an extent that he needed another hand. His first option was to ask his wife to leave the children with her mother and come to Lagos. His wife grumpily refused to move, claiming she was the type of plant that grew only in the home soil. In the circumstances, Lanuyi employed a young lady, Tanwa, as a sales assistant. She was from another village and in Lagos there were many such people. She was clever, skilful, helpful and willing to learn. Soon she was able to attend to all the routine work including typing and keeping the stores and sales records. Tanwa, prior to being employed by Lanuyi, had been living with her mother, a widow. They were able to make ends meet, as the mother was a roadside trader and she supplemented Tanwa's wages. After being employed by Lanuyi, their position improved, but unfortunately before long Tanwa's mother fell ill and died.

All alone in the world, Tanwa was devastated and was unable to cope with the ever soaring cost of living. As a temporary measure, Lanuyi gave her a room in his house. In return she did all the housework including cooking, in addition to her duties as sales assistant. But one thing led to another and Tanwa became pregnant. Lanuyi, a kind person, took her as a second wife to preserve her respectability. The cantankerous nature of his first wife doubtless contributed to his decision. The action would be in accord with a song once popular in the rural areas, which went as follows:

Agb'oko l'eri ki ipa'tete;
To ba p'atete ategun agbokolo.
Be e ategun ki i gbe iru e pa da.
Oro awa di pagidari igi da

She who can a good man catch;
Never plays with such a catch;
Otherwise she may risk a snatch;
And never again find such a match.

Besides, in those days, being a polygamist could make economic sense. Lanuyi gradually reduced his visits to the village. He continued to work hard to improve his business and to train Tunde, his new son by Tanwa, as well as to provide for those in the village. Despite these circumstances, Lanuyi did not wish to sever relations with his family back in the village and with his roots. He constantly remembered his father's advice: "Always think of the future. This is what the elders stress whenever they say that what's 'after six is more than seven'. Working away from home is like going to work at the farm. The farmer, of course, brings home the farm produce. Besides, yesterday, today and the future are inextricably linked. The events of yesterday are the stories of today that will become history in the distant future. Your roots will always be in the village. Our elders say '*Ko si ibi to 'da bi ile'* (there is no place like home). When a ship goes to sea it always returns to the harbour; never forget it."

He, therefore, had to bring Tanwa and their son to the home village. At first, it was just on occasional visits, but as his fortune improved he rebuilt his father's house. He then spent more time in the village, leaving the city business in the capable hands of Tanwa, who spent the best part of her time attending to the business. But the relations between the two wives were strained.

Tunde, Tanwa's son, grew up quickly. As he was clever like his parents he was successful in all he did. But, unfortunately for him, during his last year at secondary school his father, Lanuyi, died after a brief illness. The night before his death, Lanuyi again impressed upon his son the need for him eventually to return to the village to live, stressing that he did not wish his forbears and the family name to be forgotten there. "Besides, something tells me that doing so will considerably improve your fortune and future; you will have the last laugh over your antagonists. Promise me, my son."

"I promise, father; I shall do so." answered Tunde. "Thank you my son. You will never regret making the promise."

Out of necessity, Tunde became an adult overnight. He had to console his mother and help her with her work. As the business in Lagos was jointly owned by Lanuyi and Tanwa and was firmly in the hands of Tanwa, it was not possible for the first wife to interfere. She, therefore, as a reprisal, decided that she should inherit the rebuilt house in the village and a large part of the family farmland. She did not heed the advice given by members of the extended family. She reluctantly conceded to Tanwa and her son, Tunde, the single room in which she had lived during Lanuyi's life, and the rocky and near-barren part of the farmland near the cliff. Everybody in the village knew that nothing grew there. The small area of land was a little less than one acre, while the larger portion retained by the first wife was about five acres and yielded good crops. It was clear to everyone in the village that Tanwa and Tunde had been given a raw deal, but no one would dare to face up to the bad-tempered first wife. She was the only one who did not know that 'what is after six is more than seven'. They all knew the words of the elders, *ase'le l'abowaba,* (everyone would reap what they sowed).

In the effort to retain a connection with the village Tanwa and Tunde came home from time to time. Tunde was always singing his late father's favourite song, *'Ko si ibi to tabi ile'* (*'There's no place like home.'*) On such occasions they would be confined to their one room as the first wife did not allow them the use of the living room. They used the kitchen only at night after the first wife and her children had retired for the day. The bad-tempered first wife and her children made life difficult for Tanwa and Tunde. But for the intervention of distant relatives and neighbours, the peevish woman would have driven them out of the family home. Tanwa and Tunde persevered until in the end they could stand the ill-treatment no longer.

They resorted to renting a room and parlour in the village with a kitchen attached. Much as they tried they could not make anything grow on their farmland. But for the business in Lagos they would have become destitute, which was what the unpleasant woman

intended. She did not want 'the strangers', as she referred to Tanwa and her son, to live in the village. She wanted them to go into oblivion.

As their farmland was near the village, Tanwa and her son decided to build a cottage on it to save the rent and to have a permanent home of their own in the village. They started by fencing the area. It took another two years before they had saved enough money to start building. In the course of the work they discovered that they needed to break part of the rock to create enough space for the house. This cost them a lot in terms of toil, as they could not afford to hire the modern machinery and expertise required. They had to depend on local labour and their own efforts to undertake the work.

As the rainy season had started, the labourers could not make fast progress with the work. Tunde became discouraged; he was always nagging about the delay caused by the rain. Tanwa's remark on such occasions was *'t'olorun ba nse ore a lo'n se ibi'* (we are inclined to misconstrue God's intervention). One day after a very heavy downpour they had to send the labourers home early. When the rain eventually eased in the late afternoon the labourers were nowhere to be found. As a result Tanwa and Tunde had to continue the work on their own. Very late in the evening, they decided to call it a day and returned home. As Tunde climbed onto the edge of the rock to recover his *dansiki* he felt his feet sinking into the soft soil. He wondered how this could be on such rocky ground. What had happened was that a very large tree had become uprooted on that spot decades previously, leaving a large deposit of soil that had become covered with tall grass and other plants and the ground had compacted over time. As Tunde fought to free himself, he got more deeply embedded into the earth and the more he tried the worse it became and the deeper he sank. With a mighty heave, and with both arms clutching the solid ground on both sides, he thought that he would manage to pull himself up; but instead he fell into a cavity inside the rock. He had to shout very loudly, over and over again, to attract his mother's attention. Tanwa heard him and came to help. Tunde cautioned her not to come too near. He explained what had happened and asked her to go home to fetch a lantern and a coil of strong rope which he had in his room.

When Tanwa returned with the lantern and rope, she grumbled that she could not persuade anyone to come with her. Tunde's remark was, "Just as well," as he did not wish anyone to know about their predicament or the cave. He then asked his mother to tie one end of the rope securely around an *iroko* tree standing nearby and to throw the other end down to him. With a great deal of effort by both of them, during which poor Tanwa slipped several times and bruised herself and Tunde's hands became badly chafed by the rough rope, he was eventually pulled out. Fortunately he had found some huge stones in the cave; he had arranged them into a pile and stood on them. The pile made it easier for him to clamber up the wall of the cave while Tanwa pulled, but it was still an ordeal.

Early the following day, Tunde came to the farm and covered the opening as best as he could. This was to prevent any chance passers-by from noticing anything unusual. He again cautioned the mother that no-one was to be told about their discovery. He said that while in the dark cave he had felt some things with his feet. He would, therefore, like to explore the cave thoroughly.

The workers and the other labourers were dismissed rather early that day. As soon as the coast was clear, Tunde removed the leaves and branches, put in place a ladder he had borrowed and cautiously descended into the cave holding a lighted lantern. Meanwhile,

Tanwa sat down to wait patiently. Tunde could not believe his eyes: littering the floor were piles of rubble covering what proved to be bags and wooden boxes, all coated and caked with dust. The first box he opened was rotten, so were all the other boxes and bags. They were all filled with clothes, but also contained a huge amount of money in the form of coins as well as jewellery, valuable necklaces and hand chains made of coral and gold. He pinched himself to make certain that he was not dreaming. He then noticed a narrow path leading towards the end of the rocks. He followed it and found at the end a well-studded strong door. Of course, he knew it could not be opened as it was overgrown with weeds and shrubs. He turned back. He then recalled his mother's reaction when he went on about the incessant rains.

When he told his mother what he had found, she too was astounded. While he kept watch, he requested the mother to go to the night market and purchase some jute sacks. On her return he climbed back into the underground cavity and carefully placed as much of the treasure as he could into the bags. He made several trips up and down the ladder before he could bring up all the bags. All night they washed and cleaned the coins, jewellery and other items. While at this joyous task Tunde referred to his mother's reaction to his previous nagging. Tanwa's spontaneous reply was, 'God's ways are inscrutable'.

As all the items of clothing had become rotten they were all returned the next evening to the cave, so as to conceal them. For many evenings they repeated the search and removed the remaining useful and valuable things. It took them several more evenings to fill the cavity with earth and rubble. Fresh grass was carefully planted on the spot, to obliterate all traces. Tunde cut some tree trunks which he arranged as a form of barrier; on top of the trunks were placed the *marigbo*, palm fronds which was generally regarded as a spell; these they thought would scare nosey neighbours. A long time later Tanwa and Tunde discovered that they had stumbled upon Kasali's respository which he used during his many years as a robber and they learnt that he was the most notorious and daring bandit in the area.

On the following day, the main market day, Tanwa purchased lots of fruit of different kinds, which she said were being taken to Lagos for sale. She hired a lorry into which she loaded all the baskets, making sure that those containing the valuables they had discovered were hidden under the fruit. She and Tunde were the only travellers in the lorry. They sold the valuables, a little at a time, in Lagos.

A few years later Tunde acquired another plot of land not far away from the cottage, near the top of the hill. On it he built a more imposing house – the mansion which triggered this tale. Soon after he and Tanwa had moved into the new house, Lanuyi's old house was burnt to the ground by fire. As a result, Lanuyi's first wife and her children had to move back to her old family house in a remote part of the village, a dilapidated and overcrowded structure. Having become used to a much better standard of living they found life there really arduous. If only they had not been indolent; if only they had not alienated themselves from the extended family; if they had used the greater portion of Lanuyi's land which they had grabbed, they might have avoided this predicament. Who knows, their plight might have proved right the Yoruba saying: *sikasika gbagbe ajobi, adaniloro gbagbe ola* (the mills of God grind slowly, yet they grind exceeding fine and sure). Understandably, no-one sympathised with them; everyone thought that they were reaping what they had sowed. Fortunately Tunde and his elder half-brother, who had kept in touch with him, had a cordial relationship. Tunde made him a monthly allowance on which he, his mother and sister survived. In the meantime Tanwa and Tunde continued to work hard at the business in Lagos. They were thus able to eventually rebuild the burnt family house and enable Tunde's half-brother and the others to move back into it, to their great relief.

Tunde, meanwhile, had opened a small branch of the building materials business in the village to serve it and the other surrounding villages. His half-brother was put in charge of it. Having learnt from Tunde, he made a success of the new branch. Thanks to the rebuilt house and a steady income from the branch, the half-brother and his mother as well as his sister were able to live in reasonable comfort. The wicked woman and her daughter, thoroughly mortified, had no alternative but to call on Tanwa and Tunde one evening to ask for forgiveness for their past misdeeds and express appreciation for their rehabilitation as well as for their continued means of livelihood. In a good spirit, Tanwa and Tunde accepted their apologies and the family resumed a normal relationship.

Tanwa and Tunde were applauded by everyone in the village for their generous gesture. One of their elderly neighbours had this to say: "The events of yesterday have now become news today as they are sure to become history in the years to come. In conformity with the saying of Yoruba elders *'eyi ti owa lehin ofa oju oje lo'*, -'what's after six is more than seven' – very much more."

This seemingly simple story shows that the effects of every action or event may have momentous consequences; perhaps more than can be understood or discerned. Yes, what's after six is definitely more than seven; it could stretch to infinity.

———◆———

WHAT YOU SOW, YOU REAP

Prologue

Had the Second World War not taken place I might not have joined the Boy Scouts and I might have missed the best version of this story told by the late Chief Banjo, the *Lisa* of Sagamu, who was then Headmaster of St Pauls C.M.S. School and also Group Scoutmaster. Thanks to Hitler's War, as the Second World War was generally referred to in those days, I joined the school Wolf Cub pack in February 1942 with Teacher Soda as its *Akela*, the cub master and leader of the pack. Scouting changed my life: it provided me with a fascinating introduction to nature and the environment; it introduced me to storytelling, amongst other things, and fired my enthusiasm to master the Remo dialect of the Yoruba language. Yes, I have a lot to thank Hitler's war for. Every grey cloud has a silver lining.

In December 1941 there was a big blast in Apapa where Lagos harbour now lies. At first it was thought that the blast resulted from a bomb sent from 'German Cameroon'. It later turned out that it was due to an accident at the Apapa oil terminal. There had been some previous incidents, however, and so great was the fear and alarm that a number of schools and students were evacuated from Lagos. So, early one morning in February of 1942, I found myself on *Harmony*, one of the boats in the Rickett's fleet which plied between Lagos and Agbowa-Ikosi. I was with my Godmother and her three children. We were fleeing from Hitler's War! It provided us, the children, with no end of thrills. It was a memorable experience, though the crossing itself was uneventful. Throughout the journey the sea and the sky were blue; the waves and the foam were white with a bluish tint. It was exciting to see the puny canoes of the local fishermen alongside *Harmony*. The smell of the various foods carried by the traders was pleasant and mouth-watering.

The passengers, many carrying loads on their heads, trekked from Agbowa-Ikosi Beach to a noisy market to board the lorry which would take us on the second leg of our journey, to Sagamu. The lorry was an old and rickety contraption that had seen better days. As it was unable to climb the *Oke-Oriya* hill with its full load of goods and passengers we all had to climb down and make the ascent on foot. Occasionally the two drivers' mates threw large wooden blocks behind the tyres of the lorry to prevent it from slipping backwards! While this looked funny to us children, my Godmother did not look amused. We had to stop on a number of occasions to get our breath back. It was a great relief when the climb was completed. The awkward movements of the passengers as they attempted to clamber up into the rickety vehicle caused us children much amusement. The arduous descent was equally frightening because the hill was so steep.

We travelled on a winding, crooked and bumpy laterite road. There was not much to see for miles but trees and undergrowth; the vegetation near the road was caked with dust. But occasionally we saw squirrels and other creatures darting across the road. I had never seen so many pawpaw trees in my life! Birds were pecking at the ripe pawpaw fruit. The lorry was raising as much dust as the smoke and soot belching from its exhaust pipe. Everyone in the lorry was puffing and coughing. It was most stressful for my poor Godmother. Whenever a lorry came from the opposite direction the dust became even thicker and more irritating. It was quite a relief to get to our destination. This was a sparsely populated area which I later learnt was called Makun. It had vast green fields and many trees. It was

all very peaceful, unlike Ebute-Ero wharf in Lagos where we had embarked on *Harmony* that morning.

On the following Monday we registered at St Paul's C.M.S. School. There I joined the Wolf Cub pack at my Godmother's prompting. At my first camp, the group scoutmaster, Mr (later Chief) Banjo, widely known for his stories, told us a tale during the "yarn period", which echoed one I had previously heard from my late grandfather in 1939. A year later I was to read another version of it in *Reader III* at St Paul's Breadfruit C.M.S. School on our return to Lagos, but Pa Banjo's version was by far the best and the most interesting. It is the one that has stuck in my mind ever since.

Pa Banjo started off with a number of riddles, preceded with the usual *alo*. This ritual is the rallying call to start a story-telling session. We all responded resoundingly with *"alo"*! Then, with a smile on his genial face, and without further ado, he launched into the story, which was as thrilling as it was entertaining. It was the tale of a very good man and his wicked neighbour.

* * *

Atunda, a fast growing village on the verge of becoming a town, is on the brow of a hill which commands a good view of the surrounding area. It is perhaps the most picturesque village in the whole district. The village overlooks a very fertile area of land used for farming. The Ibu River divides this large expanse in two: the part immediately beneath the hill is used for farming, while the other side, Igbo-Eri, "forest by the river," is a huge plantation with different varieties of banana and plantain; oil palms and two other varieties of palm which produce palm-wine (*oguro* and *aran*); and trees known locally as *gedu* which provide hardwood timber. The forest teems with game and other animals.

163

Multi-coloured birds can be seen twittering, singing and flying between the trees. Monkeys of all sizes and colours jump from tree to tree. The forest abounds with innumerable butterflies of varying colours.

Most of the men in the village divide their time between farming and hunting. The village also has some full-time fishermen. There are a few others who also fish for pleasure as well as to provide for their own needs. The farmers grow maize, cassava, yams, groundnuts, tomatoes and vegetables.

Atunda market is very popular for palm oil, farm products, game and fresh fish. The village also has blacksmiths who make farming tools – hoes, cutlasses, knives, traps, buckets - as well as fishing hooks and *sakabula,* the locally made gun. In addition, the village boasts of other artisans – bricklayers, painters, carpenters and tailors. Many migrate from neighbouring cities to live in the rural areas due to the high cost of living. This has boosted the number of artisans in Atunda and increased its population. The women not involved with farming sell farm products: fresh and smoked fish; fresh and smoked game meat – this is the most popular - ; and home-cooked food such as *moyinmoyin, sagidi* (cooked and blended beans) and *edenru* (roast meat). Atunda is a very dynamic, friendly and lively community, which welcomes visitors and strangers. So it has a lot of 'foreigners' – the indigenes call them *ajeji* – living side by side with the locals.

By far the most popular man in Atunda is Asore "the one who takes delight in being good". This nickname is the result of his friendliness, helpfulness and great hospitality. The normal greeting when he is seen is *'Asore ma seka'* (He who does good and never evil). His usual answer is *'Eni se rere se fun ara re, eni se ika se fun ara re. Atore atika ikan ki i gbe'* (He who does what is good or evil will reap the appropriate benefit). He is the sole distributor of snuff for Atunda and its environs and from this he earns a good income. By local standards everyone thinks he is rich. Like most men in Atunda he also farms.

His nearest neighbour is Maku whom nearly everyone refers to as *Osika alawada* (the wicked joker who rejoices in evil), a nickname which is apt because of his wicked ways. Although he is a tailor, he also farms. Maku is a mischievous person, fond of senseless practical jokes. Because of these and his other bad qualities he has become notorious. Osika is also well known for his negativity.

After attending to customers in his store in the mornings until just before noon, Asore goes to his farm which is near the village. Whenever anyone passes by his farm, Asore will greet him and invite him to take some snuff from his pouch, which he usually hangs on a tree nearby. He makes no charge for the snuff: it is a sort of promotion for his snuff business. Thus the fame of Asore, the good man, spread far and wide. Perhaps the only person who does not like him is his neighbour, Maku, the bad man. The more popular Asore becomes, the more envious Maku is of him. Though pretending to be Asore's friend, he is only waiting for the opportunity to harm him.

On this particular evening most of the men are already home from their farms. Braziers and fireplaces are already glowing and the sweet smell of food is wafting in the air. While the women are busy with their cooking, the men, as usual, are in front of Maku's house for the first round of the evening's *ayo* game.

Ayo is played on a board about twenty-four inches long by six inches wide. There are six holes each on both sides of the board. At the start of the game, each hole has four *ayo* seeds in it. The main aim is for one of the two players to accumulate as many of the seeds as possible. Each plays in turn. Each tries to block the other by making it difficult for the opponent to accumulate seeds, that is by having more than one seed at any given time in any one hole. Whenever this happens the player collects the two or three seeds as the case may be. The winner is the one with the most seeds in the end. Although the game is between two players, each player has a number of supporters on his side. There is usually a running commentary on each side during the game by each supporter's group to motivate and encourage the player whom the group supports as well as to intimidate the opponent. Some groups even play drums. The activities of such supporters' groups can sometimes become rowdy. When a player has been beaten, another takes his place. This goes on until a champion player emerges. There are varying forms of the game and versions of it are played all over Africa.

Maku is one of the most skilful players. He comes out as champion most nights. Not only is Maku an adept at the game, he also has a stock of jokes. On many occasions it is Asore who provides the large gourd of palm wine, which passed around during the game - this drink is very good for lubricating the throat . Usually there is a break during which the men go home for the evening meal. More often than not the game continues after the meal until very late.

On that eventful day Asore plans to finish harvesting his crop of yams by the evening, but feeling tired he decides to go home early. So he starts putting all his implements into his basket: hoe, cutlass, and fly-whisk, and also his farm clothes. He is just about finishing when he hears the shuffling of feet; then a head appears. Almost immediately, comes the usual greeting: *asore ma seka*. It is his neighbour Maku. "It is rather late. I hope there's no problem?" says Asore.

"There are a few things I need to complete, as I shall not be around tomorrow," replies Maku. Asore offers him water and snuff as is his usual practice. The special thing about Asore's water is that it comes from an *amu*, a clay pot, which makes the water cool. After drinking the water Maku goes behind the tree to help himself to some snuff. He returns and bids Asore goodbye.

Soon after, Asore hears someone else approaching from the farm. Agbe, Maku's son, appears. He looks weary and very much unlike himself. In reply to Asore's question if all is well, he flops down on the green grass leaning his back against a tree. He explains that he is feeling faint and lifeless. Asore goes into his hut and brings him some water.

"Did you bring sufficient food to the farm?" he asks, "You look terrible."

"You are right, I feel terrible," Agbe replies.

Asore then also offers him some palm-wine as he thinks that will give him some energy. He then presses him to have some roasted yam as well. This is because he suspects that the young fellow is starving. Agbe accepts the kind offer, eats the yam and drinks the palm-wine. "I am sure that with the refreshment and a little rest you will soon feel better," says Asore. He then goes off to finish his packing. "Call me whenever you feel you have had enough rest and think you have sufficient strength to start the homeward journey." Soon after, Agbe calls out to say that they should start for home.

"May I have a little snuff to cheer me up?"

"Of course, help yourself," answers Asore.

He is just placing the basket inside the hut when he hears Agbe screaming, "I've been bitten by a snake." Asore quickly throws down the basket and rushes to the scene. On asking where the snake is, Agbe points to the hanging pouch. "Show me your wrist," Asore says. He then sits Agbe down and goes into the hut for his *agboyi*, a shaving knife. He bleeds Agbe, applies ground snake-poison antidote, and then tightly binds the wrist as well as his hand just below the elbow. He then asks Agbe to lift his hand and hold on to the back of his neck as if wearing an arm sling. He opens Agbe's mouth and from his medicine horn pours into it a small amount of liquid snake-bite antidote. He also binds the snuff pouch tightly so that the snake doesn't escape. They then start the homeward journey along the crooked, rough footpath with Agbe leaning heavily on Asore. Fortunately as they get on to the footpath leading to the village they see two young lads who offer to carry Agbe. Within a few minutes they get into the lane where Asore and Maku live.

That night the *ayo* game is a special one due to the presence of *Alagba* (Revered elder) Kale, the former *ayo* champion. On his arrival the old man greets them saying *"Mo k'ota, mo kope"* (" I greet both the champion and the underdog.") They answer *"Ota nje, ope ole fohun"*, (" The champion thanks you while the underdog is unable to speak.") He then sits down to watch the contest. Everyone can hear Maku's ringing voice asking Ade to wake up and play. The latter replies, "Take it easy. I need to think."

Maku: "He who does not understand *Ifa* divination

170

always looks blank."

Ade: "Be patient; more haste makes less speed."

Maku: "Go and learn how to play this game. You ought to have done so before coming to play."

Ade: "Osika, you are being yourself; I know all about your ways. Don't try to stampede me. The snail is known for taking measured steps."

Maku: "You don't know who you're playing with. A child like you cannot lift the skull of an elephant, let alone carry it."

Ade: "Yes, an elephant may give a monkey a disdainful look; but everyone knows that a monkey is not a beggar."

Maku: "Oh, come on, play, dear talkative one. By the time I finish with you no one will recognise you."

Alagba: "Softly, softly. One does not play with one's child and go out into the bush to cut branches to make whips."

Maku: "Revered elder, Ade does not know his opponent. I once told him that a baby elephant calf should not trumpet whilst its parent is doing the same thing. Let me teach my untutored opponent some sense."

Looking towards Ade, he adds in his jeering voice

with its peculiar ringing tone, "You need to practice some more before you play with a master player. That's what I am!" He again looks up, and turns his head. "Ah, here comes my good neighbour, but why the crowd? Why is he being carried? I hope he hasn't fainted." Turning to his opponent he continues, "Come on. Stop wasting time!"

The procession with Asore in the lead walks past Asore's house towards Maku's house. When Maku sees Asore on his feet he jumps up from his seat and runs to meet him.

"Maku, there has been a disaster. Agbe has been bitten by a snake," reports Asore.

Maku hastily brings out a mat on which they gently lay the groaning Agbe. Asore then goes on to explain all about the incident, adding that Agbe has been given snake-poison antidote both in powder and liquid forms.

"Quickly, call the traditional doctor," shouts Maku.

Ade runs speedily to fetch the doctor who arrives immediately and starts treating Agbe. While doing so Agbe's other hand falls limply to his side. After turning him over and looking into his eyes, the doctor pronounces Agbe dead.

There is a great hush. Then everyone starts to shout and to ask anew how it all happened. Asore recounts what happened all over again . . . ending by saying "Maku was the last person before Agbe to take snuff from the pouch."

At this point Maku slumps to the ground, and starts weeping and wailing.

"What have I done? I have with my own hand killed my only son, my very dear son."

"What do you mean?" asks everyone simultaneously.

With a haggard look he confesses his crime: "*I put the snake in the pouch with the intention of killing Asore.*"

First observer: "You have reaped what you have sown. He who sets out to hurt another may injure himself."

Second Observer: "Ashes flow towards the thrower."

Third Observer: "The wicked man who lurks in ambush to murder someone else may end up committing suicide."

Alagba: "Fellows, this is a disastrous thing. Yes, very bad. While we sympathise with Maku we must learn lessons from this happening. We must avoid doing evil and instead concentrate on doing good. As this incident has demonstrated, you reap what you sow. Maku, may

173

God console you. May he have mercy on us all. Amen."

First Observer: "Our elders say that the baldness of the vulture has nothing to do with the barber."

The crowd disperses slowly one by one, leaving Maku with the great grief which has now replaced his previous jests and jeers, and also leaving him with the corpse of his only son. His usually shining face with its twinkling eyes now looks dull, subdued and gloomy. Just one solitary person, Asore, remains to console the wretched, grieving father. Asore's parting words are these:

"Time has come for you to change. Do not lose heart: while there's life there's hope. Pull yourself together; work hard at being good. The Almighty Father will be with you in your trying moments. He will have mercy on you. He will forgive you. As for me, I have already forgiven you." In the Remo dialect this is even more beautiful, and runs like this:

Maku asiko ti to neyin nati tun wa se o. Ma bara je; ke e ku use tan, so o ma sara girin. Edumare ninu anu re a duro te e, asanu re, adari je e. Emi nite mi mo ti fori je e.

THE QUEST FOR THE RARE LEAF
AND OTHER YORUBA TALES

THE LAST MIRACLE

It was my first picnic at the High School in Lagos. We were at the Bar Beach, the famous Bar Beach with its white sand. It was Easter 19…. and it was a gorgeous day. It was bright and the sun was high up in the sky which was clear and blue, as was the sparkling sea. After the hustle and bustle of the events scheduled for the morning, after lunch we were given an hour of free time to rest. I felt restless and walked rather aimlessly towards the Kuramo Waters end of the Bar Beach.

As I walked along the side of the lagoon with its mango, cashew, paw-paw and sharp-sharp trees, I felt a sense of utter peace. It was all quiet and serene, unlike the noise of the seaside. As I emerged on the lagoon side I saw an old man sitting on a boulder near a crag at the point where the sea and the lagoon met. Separating the two was a rippling line of froth, bluish white in colour. It was a most beautiful sight to see the meeting point of the lagoon and the sea: one side green with its gentle emerald tinted ripples; the other blue with its white froth and a touch of azure. It was like a dividing line drawn by nature itself. It was all calm, cool and peaceful. There sat the old man precariously as if he would fall into the foaming sea any moment. He was scantily dressed and on his head was a cap perched at a jaunty angle.

Although, the sun was warm, curiously enough the old man was shivering. As I walked towards him I heard a sound like the uneven ticking of a clock. With concentration I soon discovered that it was the chattering of the remnants of the old man's teeth. He looked weary and unreal, like something from another world. Was this the old man of the sea? I then stood still, petrified and rooted to the ground. I pondered whether he was indeed human, or perhaps he might be a phantom. While still contemplating his other worldliness, I was startled, when the old man suddenly shouted:

"Young lad, what are you looking at? Haven't you ever seen a lonely old man before? Why are you staring at me?" I was so taken aback and paralysed with fear I could not say a word. "Are you dumb? Speak, say something," he added.

I answered almost in a whisper, "I am sorry sir, terribly sorry. You caught me by surprise." While speaking, I quickly doffed my school cap as the Reverend Roberts, the vice Principal, had taught us to as a mark of respect to elders.

"Ah! What a good boy, courteous too", the old man said, surprisingly, in a cultured voice. "Come nearer; who are you?" he asked. I told him that I was member of a group from my school on a picnic to celebrate Easter.

"Ah! Easter! Are you a Christian? What do you know about Jesus Christ?" he asked. I thought silently to myself: 'What would I know about Jesus Christ'. "I am neither the Vicar nor the Sunday School Superintendent," I muttered under my breath. Although the old man's peremptory manner of speaking had disconcerted me,. I reeled out what I had learned at Sunday School for the benefit of the old man – how Christ was born in Bethlehem of Judea, in the manger; how the large and luminous star heralded his birth; how the wise men from the East came to worship him and brought him gifts; how Mary and Joseph, his parents, ran away with him to Egypt to prevent wicked King Herod from killing the infant; how He grew up and taught in the synagogues; how He went about with His disciples preaching and healing the sick; how, out of envy, He was arrested and taken before Pilate; how He was tried and condemned to death by the

179

Roman Governor; how He was crucified, buried and was raised up on the third day; and how He finally ascended to heaven.

As I was recounting these events the old man was nodding his head; he had a faraway look on his face; occasionally he would smile and his face became tender. I saw him being gradually transformed. The grotesque and frightening old man metamorphosed. In his place was a new person, a wise man with a benign face. He beckoned to me and said, "Come and sit by me. I am impressed by your knowledge of the Holy Book and you are so tender in years. I may as well entrust you with the treasure. You know what a treasure is?" he asked. I explained as far as my understanding of the word went at that time, that a treasure is something valuable and not easily come by. I lost my former fear of the old man and sat down by him as he bade me.

"Yes, you will do", he said as if speaking to himself. "I will entrust the secret to you. I want to pass it on as I have the premonition that my time is fast approaching. It won't do for the secret to go with me. I am going to tell you a story that perhaps no other living being in this world knows. I was told this story by an angel when I was a youth. He asked me to pass it on to a young lad when my time comes.

"Something tells me that now is the time and that you are the lad. I want to be sure though," he then added. "Before I go on, I want you to answer me a question. Which was the last miracle that Jesus Christ performed?" I quickly remembered the incident which took place on the Mount of Olives, when the ear of Malchus, the servant of the Chief Priest, was cut off, adding that after Jesus had admonished the offending disciple, who wielded the sword, He put the ear back in place and Malchus was healed.

The old man smiled. "That is what many would say. But that was not the last miracle of our Lord."

He said slowly. "Come with me, back in time to Jerusalem. There on the road that led to the market place not far from Golgotha sat a blind beggar. He was begging rather noisily for alms. Then he heard the footsteps of someone approaching. "Good day friend," he said "What has happened to Jerusalem? I have sat here from early morning as is my normal practice and until now hardly has anyone passed this way. It is most unusual; I have taken no alms this day. What has gone wrong?" he lamented.

"Are you a stranger in Jerusalem? Why should

anyone come this way when all the fun is on the way to Golgotha," the person replied.

"Golgotha, that loathsome place. Why would people want to go there?" the beggar asked.

"You must be the only ignorant fool in Jerusalem. That preacher and rabble-rouser who called himself the Messiah, the Christ and son of God is being crucified. Had you sat on the road leading to Golgotha this day you would have made good takings," the speaker observed.

"Good son of Abraham lead me there. It is not yet too late" the beggar begged.

And so the mocker led the beggar as they moved towards the place of the skull.

At last they reached the vast field.

"How goes it son? Is it all over?" panted the beggar.

"No, a Roman soldier is descending the ladder. The show is still on," replied the mocker.

"May the God of Jacob reward you; please lead me closer. Although I cannot see, I want to get the feel, so that in days to come, I shall be able to say that I was there when the blasphemer was crucified. Indeed, he will destroy the temple and rebuild it in three days. That was what the Chief Priest reported that he said.

The precious temple that our fathers toiled to build in forty years and six. He deserves to die."

Slowly the mocker led the blind wretch by the hand as both tottered towards the sacred spot on which the Saviour was crucified. Nearer and nearer, they went to the cross as if drawn by some unknown power.

"Holy Moses," said the mocker.

"The criminal is still talking. I can see his lips moving."

"What is he saying?"

The soldiers and others are laughing. The mocker was talking to himself. Then he shouted loudly.

"Old man, please walk faster or else I shall leave you to the mercy of the crowd. I do not want to miss what remains of the fun."

"May the God of Abraham reward you abundantly dear brother; have patience with a blind old man".

At that point, the mocker shouted. "Hey! He has been pierced on the side with a spear."

"By whom?" asked the blind man.

"By one of the soldiers. It must be part of the punishment ordered by Pilate. Holy Moses, so much blood and water gushing from his side. Who would have thought that such a thin fellow had so much in him," added the mocker.

183

"Gentle son of Isaac, please lead me to the foot of the cross so that I may have the pleasure of striking him, only on the foot. I still have enough strength in this old arm to do justice to such a felon," begged the beggar.

Curiously enough, the soldiers and other onlookers did not stop them. The blind old wretch clutched the mocker's hand tightly. He raised the other hand and slapped the Lord on the foot just as the mixture of water and blood was trickling down. Both splashed unto the sinner's eyes. Suddenly the beggar loosened his grip on the mocker's hand and reeled backwards.

"What is the matter now?" bawled his companion. "I have no strength to carry anyone with an epileptic fit." At this moment, the blind beggar leapt into the air yelling.

"I must be running mad. I can see! Are these not three men hanging on the crosses? The one in the middle, the one whose foot I smote, he looks like an angel. His blood has restored my sight. This is the Saviour! This is the horn of salvation foretold by the prophets. What calamity have I called on my head." He ran forward like a man possessed and clung to the base of the Cross; tears running down his cheeks,

"My Lord, my Saviour, good Rabbi," he wailed. "Please forgive me. I have sinned; I mocked him; I slapped him. Who will purge me of my sin?"

While this tirade was going on, the mocker stood dumbfounded.

"If the old rogue, the beggar, could really see, then he is no sinner. What disaster have I called on my head; I mocked him. What does it all portend? The world is coming to an end," he moaned with great fear in his voice.

Suddenly, a great darkness engulfed the entire surroundings; utter silence prevailed. Then a loud pealing clash of thunder, like the roaring of a thousand lions, shattered the silence. This was followed by a heavy downpour of rain accompanied by lightning that lit up the scene. The precious blood of the Saviour mingled with the pool of water formed at the base of the cross.

The wretch, the blind beggar, no longer blind, was rolling in the pool of blood stained water. He was moaning, "Please cleanse me, Saviour. Wash away my guilt. Cleanse me from head to toe. Wash away all my mockery and misdeeds. Great Saviour, giver of life, light and sight imbue me with new life so that I may live to testify to this miracle throughout the world."

Suddenly the old man telling me the wonderfully strange story of the last miracle had got up abruptly and was walking away from me. At this point I came to myself. I quickly got up and ran after him. "Sir," I said. "Thank you; thank you Sir." I then asked the old man why old Pa Green, the Sunday School Superintendent or the Vicar had not told us this story.

"My boy, they could not have told you what they did not know. It was told to me by an angel long ago. I was ordered in the early hours this morning to pass it onto you because you are destined to become a preacher of the Gospel. May the good Lord bless you and all that is yours. May you serve long and faithfully in his vineyard."

All I could say to this unbelievable story was, "God bless you too, Sir." I stood there surprised and overwhelmed as I saw the old man walking away. He was still shaking, hugging himself and looking into thin air as one seeing things unseen by human eyes.

———————◆◆———————

I KNOW
A story from Europe

The morning was misty and frosty. The road was deserted except for a man and a horse. The unkempt man, clad in shabby clothes, was leading an old horse and as he shuffled along he appeared to be muttering to himself. A closer look, however, revealed that he was talking to the horse. "Old and loyal friend, I am sorry that it has come to this, I had hoped that we would continue the journey together until we both dropped dead. I am afraid this cannot be so. I have not even a penny in my pocket, let alone enough to buy food for both of us this morning. Hopefully at the end of this journey I shall receive something to help me keep body and soul together for perhaps another week. After that I shall lay me down in old Bernard's disused barn and sleep for ever. For the sake of old friendship I am sure you will not grudge Ted one more week."

To this speech the old horse, understandably, could not make a response, except to roll its sorrowful eyes and neigh from time to time. Ted continued, "Never mind old pal, we shall soon arrive at the yard and good-byes will be said." He stopped to caress the horse; he gently stroked its neck while tears were streaming down his sallow cheeks. Horse and man shared a common grief. Completely engrossed in the heartbreaking farewell, he was oblivious of his surroundings. He was awakened when he heard a voice.

"Who are you, my man? And what are you doing abroad so early on such a raw morning as this?" said a man standing in front of him.

"It is only fair that I should take a befitting farewell from an old and loyal friend like Tack," Ted answered.

"Why so?" the man asked.

"Tack and I spent so many years together in the rag-and-bone trade. Now he is old and broken-down; we are both broken-hearted. I can no longer afford to feed him and he is too old to be put to work. I am taking him to the knacker's yard to be put to sleep. It's only natural that I should feel sorry, dejected and lonely," he moaned.

"Can I make you a bargain?" the man asked.

"What may that be?" Ted replied suspiciously.

"I need an old horse just like yours and I wish to buy it," the man replied.

"How can you joke at a time like this?" Ted interrupted.

"I am in real earnest; I shall pay you handsomely. If you are interested in my offer here is my card. All you need to do is report at the address shown on it at seven o'clock this evening".

"How do I know that you are serious? And what do we eat, Tack and me, between now and dusk?"

"Here is a sovereign for a start; come at seven tonight and put me to the test."

Ted looked at the gold coin, bewildered. He muttered to himself, "Is this man a crank or an imbecile?" He later consoled himself by saying, "I shall spend another day with Tack with good meals for both of us to go with it; besides, I shall have a bottle of good beer". He then turned back and shuffled along with Tack in tow.

For the rest of the morning and all afternoon Ted was restless: he was forever asking passers-by for the time and the right direction of the address shown on the card. At last it was half past six. He walked along with Tack, this time with a spring in his step. Was he not about to come into money? Or was this a cruel jest? All too soon he concluded, "I shall find out the truth of the matter; before we know it old Ted may come into a fortune."

And so he arrived at no. 29 ... Street. He could not

191

believe his eyes or senses. Before him was a long stretch of high wall. The iron entrance gate was securely locked. He hesitated before timidly pulling the bell. Soon he could hear the clanging of the bell in the distance. After a few minutes a man appeared at the gate. Unceremoniously he told Ted, "Be off with you my man; what do you mean by pulling the bell and disturbing me?"

"I am here to see the owner of this house," Ted said.

"What owner?" the surly young man countered. "You must be out of your mind; this is Sir Jacob's mansion. As if Sir Jacob would receive the likes of you."

"And so what?" Ted replied. "He gave me this card and asked me to report here at seven. It is only a minute or two to seven and I do not want to be late."

Still hesitant, the man took the card. After looking at it he exclaimed, "I'll be damned! It's indeed Sir Jacob's card. Wait while I tell Mr. James, the butler." The gate clanged shut.

A few minutes after, Ted could hear the sound of feet approaching. The gate opened and he was invited in by the young man. "Come in, Mr. James will see you" he said. Ted's face lighted up and the expression on his face seemed to be saying, "I told you so." Up they went along the pathway. As they turned a bend he saw before him a large building, in front of which was a lush green lawn. The hedges were neatly trimmed and the flower beds were like pictures he had seen. At the main door stood an elderly man with grey hair. He was elegantly dressed and he had an incredulous look on his face.

"How did you come by this card?" the butler asked. "The owner, I presume, gave it to me this morning," Ted replied. With disbelief still showing on his face Mr. James asked, "What did the gentleman who gave you the card look like?" Ted was about to burst out with indignation when the gentleman himself, Sir Jacob appeared behind the butler.

"James, allow the man to come in; I asked him to come. I have been waiting for him this last half hour," said Sir Jacob.

"Very well, Sir Jacob. I shall ask the groom to tie up his horse and then bring him in," replied James.

"That will not be necessary," said Sir Jacob. "Bring both man and horse in."

Consternation was written on the faces of both Ted and the butler. "Whoever heard such a thing before; asking this unkempt tramp with a funny horse into the hallway of a rich man's home?" muttered the butler. After a discreet cough, he invited the pair in. Sir Jacob walked towards the grand staircase and said, "Follow me." Ted looked perplexed and fixed his eyes on the butler who was staring at Sir Jacob.

"Quickly, I have no time to waste," said Sir Jacob. "Hurry, bring them up the stairs." At this point both Ted and the butler felt convinced of the insanity of Sir Jacob and they were torn between the urge to scream or to make a dash for the door. Sir Jacob, without as much of a backward glance, continued to walk up the stairs and he proceeded along the carpeted corridor. When he looked back he was surprised to see Ted and the horse so far behind. As for the butler, he was rooted to the bottom of the staircase. "Make it snappy my man," Sir Jacob said, "everything must be completed before eight." Then Sir Jacob stopped in front of a white door with a brass handle. He pushed the door wide open and invited both man and beast in.

Ted was now in a quandary; he wanted to rush out of the door as he was convinced that he was with a maniac. He thought he must be correct, as the butler, maintaining a stony silence, kept away from both of them. Ted was awakened from his reverie when Sir

Jacob said, "Come across into the bathroom."

"May the holy angels protect me," Ted muttered. Moving as in a dream he walked across the elegant room and found himself in a marble panelled bathroom. A dressing table with gilded mirror was to the left just beneath the two wide windows and a marble bath was to the right.

"Please, quickly haul up the horse into the bath," said Sir Jacob. Ted obeyed like a man hypnotized. Just as he was about to scream two things occurred. The butler, who had hitherto maintained his distance, peeped into the bathroom and about the same time Sir Jacob calmly pulled out from his pocket a pistol Ted flew towards the door and fell into the arms of the butler who was rooted to the floor petrified. When the shot rang out the two made for the corridor and scampered down the stairs. They were firmly resolved to reach the garden before the pistol was turned on them.

Somehow at the bottom of the staircase, they both stopped and looked upwards. There was Sir Jacob smiling contentedly to himself and slowly walking down towards them. Again they made a dash for the main door. Then Sir Jacob called, "James, please bring our visitor into my study."

"Yes, Sir Jacob," he replied mechanically. Ted knocked at the door of the study and was asked to come in. He peeped into the room before venturing in; he then took off his cap which had all along remained glued to his head. Sir Jacob sat on a satin covered chair and was counting some money from a box unto the oak table. When he finished counting he pushed the money towards Ted. "Count it, my man, it's all there; the fifty gold sovereigns belong to you. I wish you the joy of them and I thank you warmly from the bottom of my heart."

Ted was more puzzled than ever. Without touching the money he said:

"Gov, may I ask a question?"

"Sure, ask." Sir Jacob replied. "Why do you want to give fifty sovereigns away for an old nag which by the way, you have since shot dead."

For answer Sir Jacob chuckled to himself and said, "It is a pity, my man, that you will not be here at eight o'clock when my brother Thomas, Mr Know All, returns from the city. He will in his usual way, come up the staircase with his jaunty strides. He will enter the bathroom to wash imaginary dirt from his shapely hands. For once, he will be unable to continue with his daily ritual. Instead, he will make for the staircase, now jumping two, perhaps three stairs at a time. He will burst into the drawing room putting with a frightened almost demented look and he will whisper, "Jay, there is a dead horse in my bath." It is a pity you will not be here to see it all and hear me say calmly and soberly with a flourish of my hand, "I know."

THE END

Design Management: OsanNimu
Illustration: Phil Wrigglesworth
Graphic Design: Leo Cooper, Angela Lyons
Design Direction: Ayo Alaka
Printed in India by Imprint Digital Ltd.